Advancing Maths for AQA

MECHANICS 5

Ted Graham, Aidan Burrows and Brian Gaulter

Series editors
Roger Williamson   Sam Boardman   Graham Eaton
Ted Graham   Keith Parramore

Heinemann

Heinemann Educational Publishers
a division of Heinemann Publishers (Oxford) Ltd,
Halley Court, Jordan Hill, Oxford OX2 8EJ

OXFORD JOHANNESBURG BLANTYRE MELBOURNE
AUCKLAND IBADAN GABORONE PORTSMOUTH NH (USA)
CHICAGO

First published in 2002

06 05 04 03 02
10 9 8 7 6 5 4 3 2 1

ISBN 0 435 51310 9

Cover design by Miller, Craig and Cocking

Typeset and illustrated by Tech-Set Limited, Gateshead, Tyne & Wear

Printed and bound by Scotprint in the UK

Acknowledgements
The publishers and authors acknowledge the work of the writers Ray Atkin, John Berry, Sam Boardman, David Burghes, Derek Collins, Tim Cross, Ted Graham, Andy Martin, Nigel Price, Phil Rawlins, Tom Roper, Rob Summerson and Elwyn Williams of the *AEB Mathematics for AS and A Level* Series from which some exercises and examples have been taken.

The publishers' and authors' thanks are due to the AQA for the permission to reproduce questions from past examination papers.

The answers have been provided by the authors and are not the responsibility of the examining board.

About this book

This book is one in a series of textbooks designed to provide you with exceptional preparation for AQA's new Advanced GCE Specification B. The series authors are all senior members of the examining team and have prepared the textbooks specifically to support you in studying this course.

Finding your way around

The following are there to help you find your way around when you are studying and revising:

- **edge marks** (shown on the front page) – these help you to get to the right chapter quickly;
- **contents list** – this identifies the individual sections dealing with key syllabus concepts so that you can go straight to the areas that you are looking for;
- **index** – a number in bold type indicates where to find the main entry for that topic.

Key points

Key points are not only summarised at the end of each chapter but are also boxed and highlighted within the text like this:

> The scalar product of two vectors **a** and **b**, of magnitude a and b respectively, is defined as
>
> $$ab\cos\theta$$
>
> where θ is the angle measured in an anticlockwise direction between **a** and **b**. The scalar product of the two vectors **a** and **b** is denoted by **a.b**.

Exercises and exam questions

Worked examples and carefully graded questions familiarise you with the specification and bring you up to exam standard. Each book contains:

- Worked examples and Worked exam questions to show you how to tackle typical questions; Examiner's tips will also provide guidance;
- Graded exercises, gradually increasing in difficulty up to exam-level questions, which are marked by an [A];
- Test-yourself sections for each chapter so that you can check your understanding of the key aspects of that chapter and identify any sections that you should review;
- Answers to the questions are included at the back of the book.

Unless otherwise stated, where a numerical value is required, assume $g = 9.8\,\text{m}\,\text{s}^{-2}$.

CHAPTER 1

Vector methods in mechanics

Learning objectives

After studying this chapter you should be able to:

- use the scalar product to find the angle between vectors and the work done by a force
- use the vector product to find the moment of a force
- apply the vector product to two- and three-dimensional problems involving equivalent force systems.

1.1 Product of two vectors

In other modules we have considered addition and subtraction of two or more vectors and the multiplication of a vector by a scalar, such as $2(3\mathbf{i} - \mathbf{j}) = 6\mathbf{i} - 2\mathbf{j}$. In mechanics, we often need to multiply two vector quantities. For example, we have found in M2 or M3 that the work done by a force on a body is the product of the force and the distance moved by the body in the direction of the force.

For the situation shown in the diagram, where the force of magnitude F acts on a body as it moves a distance r from A to B

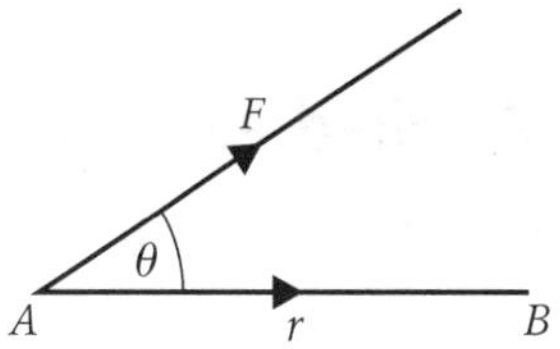

Work done $= Fr\cos\theta$

Note that the **distance** between the two points A and B is AB, which is usually considered to be the length AB. The **displacement** $\overrightarrow{AB}$ is a vector with direction $\overrightarrow{AB}$ and magnitude AB. Hence, when you consider the vector $\overrightarrow{AB}$ it should be called a displacement and not a distance.

Scalar product

The scalar product of two vectors **a** and **b**, of magnitude a and b respectively, is defined as

$$ab\cos\theta$$

where θ is the angle measured in an anticlockwise direction between **a** and **b**. The scalar product of the two vectors **a** and **b** is denoted by **a.b**.

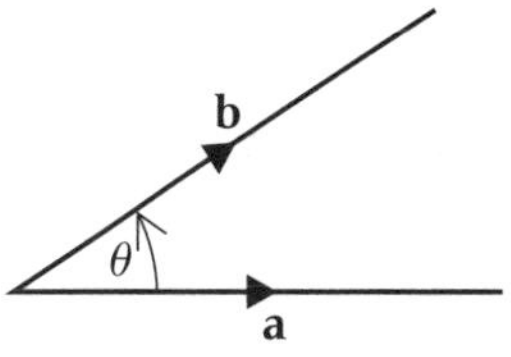

Notice that **a.b** is a scalar which is why it is called the **scalar product**. Sometimes **a.b** is also known as the **dot product**.

If **a** and **b** are perpendicular to each other, then $\theta = 90°$ and $\cos\theta = 0$ and hence $\mathbf{a}.\mathbf{b} = 0$.

If **a** and **b** are parallel to each other, then $\theta = 0°$ and $\cos\theta = 1$, so that $\mathbf{a.b} = ab$. Also $\mathbf{a.a} = a^2$.

The scalar products of the unit vectors **i**, **j** and **k** can be found. First note that,

$$\mathbf{i.i} = \mathbf{j.j} = \mathbf{k.k} = 1,$$

since these are the products of parallel unit vectors. Similarly $\mathbf{i.j} = 0$, since the angle between **i** and **j** is 90°. In the same way, $\mathbf{i.k} = \mathbf{j.k} = 0$.

$$\begin{aligned}\mathbf{a.b} &= (a_1\mathbf{i} + a_2\mathbf{j} + a_3\mathbf{k}).(b_1\mathbf{i} + b_2\mathbf{j} + b_3\mathbf{k}) \\ &= a_1\mathbf{i}.b_1\mathbf{i} + a_1\mathbf{i}.b_2\mathbf{j} + a_1\mathbf{i}.b_3\mathbf{k} + a_2\mathbf{j}.b_1\mathbf{i} + a_2\mathbf{j}.b_2\mathbf{j} + \\ &\quad a_2\mathbf{j}.b_3\mathbf{k} + a_3\mathbf{k}.b_1\mathbf{i} + a_3\mathbf{k}.b_2\mathbf{j} + a_3\mathbf{k}.b_3\mathbf{k} \\ &= a_1b_1 + a_2b_2 + a_3b_3\end{aligned}$$

Thus

$$\mathbf{a.b} = ab\cos\theta = a_1b_1 + a_2b_2 + a_3b_3$$

and

$$\mathbf{b.a} = ba\cos(-\theta) = ab\cos\theta = \mathbf{a.b}.$$

So the scalar product is commutative.

Worked example 1.1

Find **p.q** where $\mathbf{p} = 3\mathbf{i} - 6\mathbf{j} - 2\mathbf{k}$ and $\mathbf{q} = 5\mathbf{i} + 4\mathbf{j} - 8\mathbf{k}$.

Solution

$$\begin{aligned}\mathbf{p.q} &= (3\mathbf{i} - 6\mathbf{j} - 2\mathbf{k}).(5\mathbf{i} + 4\mathbf{j} - 8\mathbf{k}) \\ &= 3 \times 5 + (-6) \times 4 + (-2) \times (-8) \\ &= 15 - 24 + 16 \\ &= 7\end{aligned}$$

This scalar product is easier to calculate when the two vectors are written as column vectors;

$$\mathbf{p.q} = \begin{pmatrix} 3 \\ -6 \\ -2 \end{pmatrix} . \begin{pmatrix} 5 \\ 4 \\ -8 \end{pmatrix}$$

Here you multiply each pair of adjacent numbers.

$$\begin{aligned}&= 3 \times 5 + (-6) \times 4 + (-2) \times (-8) \\ &= 15 - 24 + 16 \\ &= 7\end{aligned}$$

The angle between two vectors

Starting with $\mathbf{a.b} = ab\cos\theta$ gives,

$$\cos\theta = \frac{\mathbf{a.b}}{ab}$$ where θ is the anticlockwise angle between the

vectors **a** and **b**. This result can be used to find the angle between two vectors.

Worked example 1.2

Find the angle between the vectors $4\mathbf{i} + 3\mathbf{j} - 12\mathbf{k}$ and $5\mathbf{i} - \mathbf{j} - 2\mathbf{k}$.

Solution

First calculate the scalar product of the two vectors.

$$\mathbf{a.b} = \begin{pmatrix} 4 \\ 3 \\ -12 \end{pmatrix} . \begin{pmatrix} 5 \\ -1 \\ -2 \end{pmatrix}$$

$$= 4 \times 5 + 3 \times (-1) + (-12) \times (-2)$$
$$= 20 - 3 + 24$$
$$= 41$$

Then calculate the magnitude of each of the vectors.

$$a = |\mathbf{a}| = \sqrt{4^2 + 3^2 + (-12)^2} = 13$$

$$b = |\mathbf{b}| = \sqrt{5^2 + (-1)^2 + (-2)^2} = \sqrt{30}$$

These values can now be substituted into the formula, $\cos\theta = \dfrac{\mathbf{a.b}}{ab}$, and used to find the angle between vectors.

$$\cos\theta = \frac{\mathbf{a.b}}{ab}$$
$$= \frac{41}{13\sqrt{30}}$$
$$\theta = 54.8^\circ$$

Worked example 1.3

Find λ if the vectors **a** and **b** are perpendicular, where $\mathbf{a} = 3\mathbf{i} - \lambda\mathbf{j} + 7\mathbf{k}$ and $\mathbf{b} = 4\mathbf{i} + 3\mathbf{j} + 3\mathbf{k}$

Solution

If **a** and **b** are perpendicular, then the scalar product of these two vectors will be zero. So begin by finding the scalar product in terms of λ.

$$\mathbf{a.b} = \begin{pmatrix} 3 \\ -\lambda \\ 7 \end{pmatrix} . \begin{pmatrix} 4 \\ 3 \\ 3 \end{pmatrix}$$

$$= 12 - 3\lambda + 21$$

$$= 33 - 3\lambda$$

As **a** and **b** are perpendicular, $\mathbf{a.b} = 0$

$$33 - 3\lambda = 0$$

$$\lambda = 11$$

Worked example 1.4

The vectors **a** and **b** are defined as $\mathbf{a} = 2\mathbf{i} + \mathbf{j} + 2\mathbf{k}$ and $\mathbf{b} = 3\mathbf{i} - 4\mathbf{j} + \lambda\mathbf{k}$.

Find λ if the angle between **a** and **b** is $\cos^{-1}\dfrac{4}{5\sqrt{2}}$.

Solution

First find the scalar product in terms of λ.

$$\mathbf{a.b} = \begin{pmatrix} 2 \\ 1 \\ 2 \end{pmatrix} . \begin{pmatrix} 3 \\ -4 \\ \lambda \end{pmatrix} = 6 - 4 + 2\lambda = 2 + 2\lambda$$

Then using $\mathbf{a.b} = ab\cos\theta$ gives

$$2 + 2\lambda = \sqrt{2^2 + 1^2 + 2^2}\sqrt{3^2 + (-4)^2 + \lambda^2}\cos\theta$$

$$= 3\sqrt{25 + \lambda^2}.\frac{4}{5\sqrt{2}}$$

$$(2 + 2\lambda)5\sqrt{2} = 12\sqrt{(25 + \lambda^2)}$$

$$5\sqrt{2}(1 + \lambda) = 6\sqrt{(25 + \lambda^2)}$$

Squaring both sides of the equation gives,

$$50(1 + 2\lambda + \lambda^2) = 36(25 + \lambda^2)$$

$$14\lambda^2 + 100\lambda - 850 = 0$$

$$7\lambda^2 + 50\lambda - 425 = 0$$

$$(\lambda - 5)(7\lambda + 85) = 0$$

$$\lambda = 5 \text{ or } -\frac{85}{7}$$

Calculating the work done using a scalar product

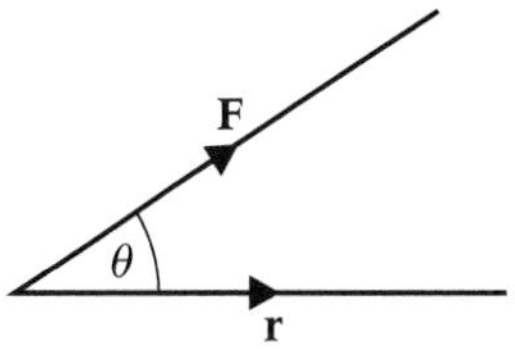

> If a force, **F**, acts on a body as its displacement changes by **r**, then the work done is $Fr\cos\theta$, where F is the magnitude of the force and r is the magnitude of the displacement.
> That is,
>
> Work done = **F.r**

The unit of work can be expressed as the **newton metre (N m)** but it is more commonly referred to as the **joule (J)**.

Worked example 1.5

Find the work done when a force $3\mathbf{i} + 2\mathbf{j} - \mathbf{k}$ acts upon a body, which moves from point A with coordinates (3, 2, 5) to point B with coordinates (7, 4, 2).

Solution

The displacement of the body is

$$\overrightarrow{AB} = \mathbf{b} - \mathbf{a}$$

$$= \begin{pmatrix} 7 \\ 4 \\ 2 \end{pmatrix} - \begin{pmatrix} 3 \\ 2 \\ 5 \end{pmatrix} = \begin{pmatrix} 4 \\ 2 \\ -3 \end{pmatrix}$$

The work done by the force is given by the scalar product of the displacement and the force.

$$\text{Work done} = \begin{pmatrix} 3 \\ 2 \\ -1 \end{pmatrix} . \begin{pmatrix} 4 \\ 2 \\ -3 \end{pmatrix}$$

$$= 12 + 4 + 3$$

$$= 19\,\text{N m}$$

Worked example 1.6

A particle moves along the line

$$\mathbf{r} = \begin{pmatrix} 3 \\ 4 \\ 2 \end{pmatrix} + t\begin{pmatrix} 1 \\ -2 \\ 2 \end{pmatrix}.$$

A force $3\mathbf{i} - 4\mathbf{j} + 5\mathbf{k}$ acts upon the particle, which initially is at the point with coordinates (3, 4, 2). Find the position of the particle when the work done by the force is 42 J.

Solution

The displacement of the particle is $\lambda\begin{pmatrix}1\\-2\\2\end{pmatrix}$.

The work done is given by **F.r**,

$$\text{Work done} = \begin{pmatrix}3\\-4\\5\end{pmatrix}\cdot\lambda\begin{pmatrix}1\\-2\\2\end{pmatrix}$$

$$= 3\lambda + 8\lambda + 10\lambda$$

$$= 21\lambda$$

Since work done is 42 J

$$21\lambda = 42$$

$$\lambda = 2$$

Hence, the displacement of the particle is $\begin{pmatrix}2\\-4\\4\end{pmatrix}$.

The particle started at (3, 4, 2).

The particle is now at (5, 0, 6).

Worked example 1.7

A block slides down a smooth inclined plane from A to B. The forces acting on the block are its weight, W, and a normal reaction, S. Calculate the work done by the forces in terms of h, the vertical height through which the block has moved.

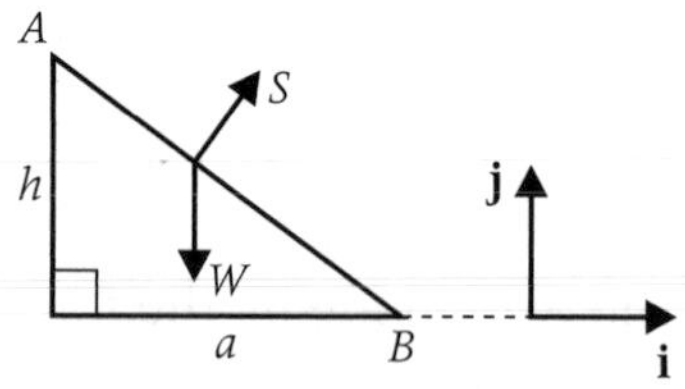

Solution

Using the perpendicular unit vectors **i** and **j** in the directions shown

$$\mathbf{W} = -W\mathbf{j} \quad \text{and} \quad \mathbf{r} = -h\mathbf{j} + a\mathbf{i},$$

$$\mathbf{W.r} = -W\mathbf{j}.(-h\mathbf{j} + a\mathbf{i}) = Wh$$

and **S.r** $= 0$ since **S** and **r** are perpendicular.

Thus, the work done is Wh.

EXERCISE 1A

In this exercise the unit vectors **i** , **j** and **k** are mutually perpendicular.

1 Find **a.b** where:

(a) $\mathbf{a} = 3\mathbf{i} - 7\mathbf{j} + 8\mathbf{k}$, $\mathbf{b} = 2\mathbf{i} + \mathbf{j} - 6\mathbf{k}$,

(b) $\mathbf{a} = 5\mathbf{i} + 2\mathbf{j} - 3\mathbf{k}$, $\mathbf{b} = \mathbf{i} - \mathbf{j} + 3\mathbf{k}$,

(c) $\mathbf{a} = 4\mathbf{i} - 7\mathbf{j} + 6\mathbf{k}$, $\mathbf{b} = 5\mathbf{i} + 7\mathbf{j} - 2\mathbf{k}$,

(d) $\mathbf{a} = \mathbf{i} + 5\mathbf{j} + 11\mathbf{k}$, $\mathbf{b} = 4\mathbf{i} + 3\mathbf{j} - 2\mathbf{k}$.

2 Find the angle between the vectors **a** and **b** when:

(a) $\mathbf{a} = \mathbf{i} - 2\mathbf{j} + 2\mathbf{k}$, $\mathbf{b} = 12\mathbf{i} + 3\mathbf{j} - 4\mathbf{k}$,

(b) $\mathbf{a} = 5\mathbf{i} + 5\mathbf{j} - 6\mathbf{k}$, $\mathbf{b} = \mathbf{i} - \mathbf{j} + 4\mathbf{k}$,

(c) $\mathbf{a} = 7\mathbf{i} - 7\mathbf{j} + \sqrt{2}\mathbf{k}$, $\mathbf{b} = 4\mathbf{i} + 6\mathbf{j} - \sqrt{2}\mathbf{k}$,

(d) $\mathbf{a} = -3\mathbf{i} + 4\mathbf{j} + 12\mathbf{k}$, $\mathbf{b} = 2\mathbf{i} + \mathbf{j} - 2\mathbf{k}$.

3 (a) Find the work done when a force $(3\mathbf{i} + 5\mathbf{j} + 2\mathbf{k})$ N acts upon a body as it is displaced $(4\mathbf{i} - 2\mathbf{j} + 4\mathbf{k})$ m.

(b) The body has a mass of 4 kg and is initially at rest. Find the final speed of the body.

4 (a) Find the work done when a force $(4\mathbf{i} - 3\mathbf{j} + 8\mathbf{k})$ N acts upon a body as it is displaced by $(2\mathbf{i} + \mathbf{j} - 3\mathbf{k})$ m.

(b) The body was initially moving at $3\,\text{m s}^{-1}$ and has a mass of 10 kg. Find the final speed of the body.

5 Find the work done when a force $(4\mathbf{i} + \mathbf{j} - 2\mathbf{k})$ acts upon a body which moves from point A with coordinates $(4, 1, -2)$ to point B with coordinates $(5, 3, 0)$.

6 Find the work done when a force $(\mathbf{i} + 4\mathbf{j} - 7\mathbf{k})$ acts upon a body which moves from point A with coordinates $(2, 4, -1)$ to point B with coordinates $(5, 5, -6)$.

7 The vectors **a** and **b** are defined as $\mathbf{a} = 2\mathbf{i} + \mathbf{j} + 2\mathbf{k}$ and $\mathbf{b} = 3\mathbf{i} - 4\mathbf{j} + \lambda\mathbf{k}$.
Find λ if **a** and **b** are perpendicular to each other.

8 The vectors **a** and **b** are defined as $\mathbf{a} = 5\mathbf{i} - 3\mathbf{j} + 2\mathbf{k}$ and $\mathbf{b} = 2\mathbf{i} + \lambda\mathbf{j} + 3\mathbf{k}$.
Find λ if **a** and **b** are perpendicular to each other.

9 The vectors **a** and **b** are defined as $\mathbf{a} = 3\mathbf{i} + 4\mathbf{j} - 12\mathbf{k}$ and $\mathbf{b} = 4\mathbf{i} - 2\mathbf{j} + \lambda\mathbf{k}$.
Find λ if the angle between **a** and **b** is $\cos^{-1}\frac{2}{3}$.

10 The vectors **a** and **b** are defined as $\mathbf{a} = \mathbf{i} + 3\mathbf{j}$ and $\mathbf{b} = 3\mathbf{i} + \lambda\mathbf{j} + 5\mathbf{k}$.
Find λ if the angle between **a** and **b** is $\cos^{-1}\dfrac{3}{2\sqrt{5}}$.

11 A particle of mass 2 kg is acted on by two forces $\mathbf{F}_1 = 3\mathbf{i} + \mathbf{j} + \mathbf{k}$ and $\mathbf{F}_2 = \mathbf{i} - 3\mathbf{j} + 2\mathbf{k}$.

(a) Find the magnitude of the resultant force on the particle and its acceleration in vector form.

(b) Find the angle between the forces $\mathbf{F}_1$ and $\mathbf{F}_2$. [A]

12 An object, of mass 40 kg, is supported in equilibrium by four cables. The forces, in newtons, exerted by three of the cables, $\mathbf{F}_1$, $\mathbf{F}_2$ and $\mathbf{F}_3$, are given in terms of the unit vectors **i**, **j** and **k** as $\mathbf{F}_1 = 80\mathbf{i} + 20\mathbf{j} + 100\mathbf{k}$, $\mathbf{F}_2 = 60\mathbf{i} - 40\mathbf{j} + 80\mathbf{k}$ and $\mathbf{F}_3 = -50\mathbf{i} - 100\mathbf{j} + 80\mathbf{k}$. The unit vectors **i** and **j** are perpendicular and horizontal and the unit vector **k** is vertically upwards. (Assume $g = 10\,\text{m s}^{-2}$.)

(a) Find $\mathbf{F}_4$, the force exerted by the fourth cable, in terms of **i**, **j** and **k**. Also find its magnitude to the nearest newton.

(b) Find the angle between $\mathbf{F}_1$ and $\mathbf{F}_4$. [A]

13 A particle, of mass 8 kg, moves so that its position, $\mathbf{r}$ m, at time t s is given by

$$\mathbf{r} = (2 + 8t)\mathbf{i} + 4t\mathbf{j} + (1 + 6t - 5t^2)\mathbf{k},$$

where **i**, **j** and **k** are three mutually perpendicular unit vectors.

(a) Show that the velocity of the particle is $8\mathbf{i} + 4\mathbf{j} + 4\mathbf{k}$ when $t = 0.2$ s. Find the velocity when $t = 0.4$ s.

(b) Find the angle between the two velocity vectors found in **(a)**.

(c) Find the magnitude of the force acting on the particle at time t. [A]

1.2 The vector product

When you multiply a force, **F**, by a displacement, **r**, both of which are vectors, you can obtain two results:

- $Fr\cos\theta$, which, as we found above, is the **work done** by the force in the direction **r**,

and

- $Fr\sin\theta$, which, including a clockwise or anticlockwise direction, is the **moment of the force**.

We have already met the scalar product.
The other product is called the **vector product**.

The **vector product** or **cross product** of vectors **a** and **b** is denoted by $\mathbf{a} \times \mathbf{b}$ or $\mathbf{a} \wedge \mathbf{b}$,
and the **vector product** is defined as $ab\sin\theta\,\mathbf{n}$ where θ is the angle in the anticlockwise sense between **a** and **b**, and **n** is a unit vector, so that **a**, **b** and **n** form a right-handed set.

Note that $\mathbf{a} \times \mathbf{b} = ab\sin\theta\,\mathbf{n}$, where **a**, **b** and **n** form a right-handed set,

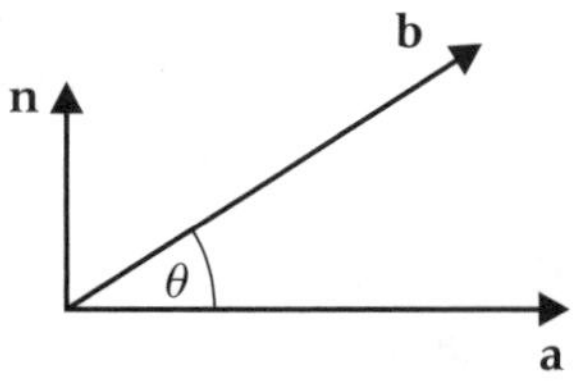

b, **a** and **n** form a left-handed set

so **b**, **a** and $-\mathbf{n}$ form a right-handed set

and $\mathbf{b} \times \mathbf{a} = ab\sin\theta(-\mathbf{n}) = -ab\sin\theta\,\mathbf{n}$

$\mathbf{a} \times \mathbf{b} = -\mathbf{b} \times \mathbf{a}$

Note also that $\mathbf{a} \times \mathbf{b} = 0 \Rightarrow$ **a** and **b** are parallel.
You will remember that $\mathbf{a.a} = a^2$ and $\mathbf{a.b} = 0 \Rightarrow$ **a** and **b** were perpendicular vectors.

Since the angle θ between $\mathbf{a}$ and $\mathbf{a}$ is zero, $\mathbf{a} \times \mathbf{a} = 0$.
Similarly $\mathbf{i} \times \mathbf{i} = 1.1 \sin\theta\, \mathbf{n} = 0$, since angle $\theta = 0$

$$\mathbf{i} \times \mathbf{i} = \mathbf{j} \times \mathbf{j} = \mathbf{k} \times \mathbf{k} = 0$$

$$\mathbf{i} \times \mathbf{j} = 1.1 \sin 90^\circ\, \mathbf{n} = \mathbf{n},$$

where $\mathbf{n}$ is a unit vector, so that $\mathbf{i}, \mathbf{j}, \mathbf{n}$ form a right-handed set.
Since $\mathbf{i}, \mathbf{j}, \mathbf{k}$ are defined as three mutually perpendicular vectors which form a right-handed set, $\mathbf{i}, \mathbf{j}, \mathbf{k}$ and $\mathbf{i}, \mathbf{j}, \mathbf{n}$ both form right-handed sets

$$\therefore \quad \mathbf{n} = \mathbf{k}$$

Hence $\mathbf{i} \times \mathbf{j} = \mathbf{k}$.

Similarly, $\mathbf{j} \times \mathbf{i} = -\mathbf{k}$,

$\mathbf{j} \times \mathbf{k} = \mathbf{i}$, $\quad \mathbf{k} \times \mathbf{j} = -\mathbf{i}$,

$\mathbf{k} \times \mathbf{i} = \mathbf{j}$, $\quad \mathbf{i} \times \mathbf{k} = -\mathbf{j}$.

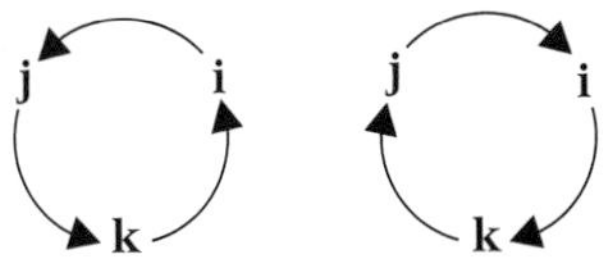

Notice that the vectors, $\mathbf{i}, \mathbf{j}, \mathbf{k}$, have a product which is positive if the order is anticlockwise, and negative if the product is clockwise.

Hence,

$$\begin{aligned}
\mathbf{a} \times \mathbf{b} &= (a_1\mathbf{i} + a_2\mathbf{j} + a_3\mathbf{k}) \times (b_1\mathbf{i} + b_2\mathbf{j} + b_3\mathbf{k}) \\
&= a_1\mathbf{i} \times b_1\mathbf{i} + a_2\mathbf{j} \times b_1\mathbf{i} + a_3\mathbf{k} \times b_1\mathbf{i} + a_1\mathbf{i} \times b_2\mathbf{j} + a_2\mathbf{j} \\
&\qquad \times b_2\mathbf{j} + a_3\mathbf{k} \times b_2\mathbf{j} + a_1\mathbf{i} \times b_3\mathbf{k} + a_2\mathbf{j} \times b_3\mathbf{k} + a_3\mathbf{k} \times b_3\mathbf{k} \\
&= a_1b_2\mathbf{k} - a_2b_1\mathbf{k} + a_3b_1\mathbf{j} - a_1b_3\mathbf{j} + a_2b_3\mathbf{i} - a_3b_2\mathbf{i} \\
&= (a_2b_3 - a_3b_2)\mathbf{i} - (a_1b_3 - b_1a_3)\mathbf{j} + (a_1b_2 - a_2b_1)\mathbf{k}
\end{aligned}$$

It is often simpler to use determinants to calculate the cross product.
You will note that

$$\begin{vmatrix} \mathbf{i} & \mathbf{j} & \mathbf{k} \\ a_1 & a_2 & a_3 \\ b_1 & b_2 & b_3 \end{vmatrix} = \mathbf{i}\begin{vmatrix} a_2 & a_3 \\ b_2 & b_3 \end{vmatrix} - \mathbf{j}\begin{vmatrix} a_1 & a_3 \\ b_1 & b_3 \end{vmatrix} + \mathbf{k}\begin{vmatrix} a_1 & a_2 \\ b_1 & b_2 \end{vmatrix}$$

$$= (a_2b_3 - a_3b_2)\mathbf{i} - (a_1b_3 - b_1a_3)\mathbf{j} + (a_1b_2 - a_2b_1)\mathbf{k}$$

which you will observe is $\mathbf{a} \times \mathbf{b}$.

$$\mathbf{a} \times \mathbf{b} = \begin{vmatrix} \mathbf{i} & \mathbf{j} & \mathbf{k} \\ a_1 & a_2 & a_3 \\ b_1 & b_2 & b_3 \end{vmatrix}$$

If you do not wish to use determinants you should remember that

$$\mathbf{a} \times \mathbf{b} = (a_2b_3 - a_3b_2)\mathbf{i} - (a_1b_3 - b_1a_3)\mathbf{j} + (a_1b_2 - a_2b_1)\mathbf{k}$$

Worked example 1.8

Evaluate $(3\mathbf{i} + 4\mathbf{j} - \mathbf{k}) \times (5\mathbf{i} - 2\mathbf{j} + 2\mathbf{k})$

Solution

$$\begin{pmatrix} 3 \\ 4 \\ -1 \end{pmatrix} \times \begin{pmatrix} 5 \\ -2 \\ 2 \end{pmatrix} = \begin{vmatrix} \mathbf{i} & \mathbf{j} & \mathbf{k} \\ 3 & 4 & -1 \\ 5 & -2 & 2 \end{vmatrix}$$

$$= \mathbf{i}\begin{vmatrix} 4 & -1 \\ -2 & 2 \end{vmatrix} - \mathbf{j}\begin{vmatrix} 3 & -1 \\ 5 & 2 \end{vmatrix} + \mathbf{k}\begin{vmatrix} 3 & 4 \\ 5 & -2 \end{vmatrix}$$

$$= 6\mathbf{i} - 11\mathbf{j} - 26\mathbf{k}$$

Worked example 1.9

Evaluate $|\overrightarrow{PQ} \times \overrightarrow{RS}|$, where P is $(2, -1, 7)$, Q is $(3, 1, 4)$, R is $(5, 1, -3)$ and S is $(-1, 2, 5)$.

Solution

$$\overrightarrow{PQ} = \mathbf{q} - \mathbf{p} = \begin{pmatrix} 3 \\ 1 \\ 4 \end{pmatrix} - \begin{pmatrix} 2 \\ -1 \\ 7 \end{pmatrix} = \begin{pmatrix} 1 \\ 2 \\ -3 \end{pmatrix}$$

$$\overrightarrow{RS} = \mathbf{s} - \mathbf{r} = \begin{pmatrix} -1 \\ 2 \\ 5 \end{pmatrix} - \begin{pmatrix} 5 \\ 1 \\ -3 \end{pmatrix} = \begin{pmatrix} -6 \\ 1 \\ 8 \end{pmatrix}$$

$$\therefore \quad \overrightarrow{PQ} \times \overrightarrow{RS} = \begin{pmatrix} 1 \\ 2 \\ -3 \end{pmatrix} \times \begin{pmatrix} -6 \\ 1 \\ 8 \end{pmatrix}$$

$$= \begin{vmatrix} \mathbf{i} & \mathbf{j} & \mathbf{k} \\ 1 & 2 & -3 \\ -6 & 1 & 8 \end{vmatrix}$$

$$= 19\mathbf{i} + 10\mathbf{j} + 13\mathbf{k}$$

$$|\overrightarrow{PQ} \times \overrightarrow{RS}| = \sqrt{19^2 + 10^2 + 13^2}$$

$$= \sqrt{630}$$

$$= 3\sqrt{70}$$

Expressing sin θ in terms of $\mathbf{a} \times \mathbf{b}$

Since $\mathbf{a} \times \mathbf{b} = ab \sin\theta\, \mathbf{n}$,

$$|\mathbf{a} \times \mathbf{b}| = |ab \sin\theta\, \mathbf{n}| = ab \sin\theta \text{ since } \mathbf{n} \text{ is a unit vector.}$$

$$|\mathbf{a} \times \mathbf{b}| = |\mathbf{a}||\mathbf{b}| \sin\theta$$

Hence, $\sin\theta = \dfrac{|\mathbf{a} \times \mathbf{b}|}{ab}$ or $\dfrac{|\mathbf{a} \times \mathbf{b}|}{|\mathbf{a}||\mathbf{b}|}$.

Worked example 1.10

By using the vector product of $\overrightarrow{AB}$ and $\overrightarrow{AC}$ find the angle between AB and AC, where A is the point with coordinates $(3, 7, 2)$, B is the point with coordinates $(2, 8, 1)$ and C is the point with coordinates $(5, 4, -1)$.

Solution

$$\overrightarrow{AB} = \mathbf{b} - \mathbf{a}$$

$$= \begin{pmatrix} 2 \\ 8 \\ 1 \end{pmatrix} - \begin{pmatrix} 3 \\ 7 \\ 2 \end{pmatrix}$$

$$= \begin{pmatrix} -1 \\ 1 \\ -1 \end{pmatrix}$$

$$\overrightarrow{AC} = \mathbf{c} - \mathbf{a}$$

$$= \begin{pmatrix} 5 \\ 4 \\ -1 \end{pmatrix} - \begin{pmatrix} 3 \\ 7 \\ 2 \end{pmatrix}$$

$$= \begin{pmatrix} 2 \\ -3 \\ -3 \end{pmatrix}$$

$$\overrightarrow{AB} \times \overrightarrow{AC} = \begin{vmatrix} \mathbf{i} & \mathbf{j} & \mathbf{k} \\ -1 & 1 & -1 \\ 2 & -3 & -3 \end{vmatrix}$$

$$= -6\mathbf{i} - 5\mathbf{j} + \mathbf{k}$$

$$\text{Using } \sin\theta = \frac{|\mathbf{a} \times \mathbf{b}|}{|\mathbf{a}||\mathbf{b}|}$$

$$\sin\theta = \frac{|-6\mathbf{i} - 5\mathbf{j} + \mathbf{k}|}{|-\mathbf{i} + \mathbf{j} - \mathbf{k}||2\mathbf{i} - 3\mathbf{j} - 3\mathbf{k}|}$$

$$= \frac{\sqrt{62}}{\sqrt{3}\sqrt{22}}$$

$$= \frac{\sqrt{62}}{\sqrt{66}}$$

$$\theta = 75.7^\circ$$

Worked example 1.11

If $\mathbf{a} = \mathbf{i} - 3\mathbf{j} + 2\mathbf{k}$ and $\mathbf{b} = -2\mathbf{i} + 6\mathbf{j} - 4\mathbf{k}$, find $\mathbf{a} \times \mathbf{b}$.
What can you deduce about $\mathbf{a}$ and $\mathbf{b}$?

Solution

$$\mathbf{a} \times \mathbf{b} = (\mathbf{i} - 3\mathbf{j} + 2\mathbf{k}) \times (-2\mathbf{i} + 6\mathbf{j} - 4\mathbf{k})$$

$$= \begin{vmatrix} \mathbf{i} & \mathbf{j} & \mathbf{k} \\ 1 & -3 & 2 \\ -2 & 6 & -4 \end{vmatrix}$$

$$= \mathbf{0}$$

Hence **a** and **b** are parallel. You can readily see that $\mathbf{b} = -2\mathbf{a}$.

EXERCISE 1B

1 Find $\mathbf{a} \times \mathbf{b}$ when:

(a) $\mathbf{a} = 5\mathbf{i} - 3\mathbf{j} + 2\mathbf{k}$, $\mathbf{b} = 7\mathbf{i} + 2\mathbf{j} - 3\mathbf{k}$,
(b) $\mathbf{a} = 2\mathbf{i} + 3\mathbf{j} - 4\mathbf{k}$, $\mathbf{b} = \mathbf{i} - \mathbf{j} + \mathbf{k}$,
(c) $\mathbf{a} = 3\mathbf{i} + 5\mathbf{j} + \mathbf{k}$, $\mathbf{b} = 2\mathbf{i} + 6\mathbf{j} - 3\mathbf{k}$,
(d) $\mathbf{a} = 2\mathbf{i} - 7\mathbf{j} + 4\mathbf{k}$, $\mathbf{b} = 3\mathbf{i} - 3\mathbf{j} + 3\mathbf{k}$.

2 By finding $\mathbf{a} \times \mathbf{b}$, find the sine of the angle between the vectors **a** and **b** when:

(a) $\mathbf{a} = 2\mathbf{i} - 2\mathbf{j} + \mathbf{k}$, $\mathbf{b} = 3\mathbf{i} + 4\mathbf{j} - 5\mathbf{k}$,
(b) $\mathbf{a} = 3\mathbf{i} - 4\mathbf{j} + \mathbf{k}$, $\mathbf{b} = 4\mathbf{i} + 3\mathbf{j} - 2\mathbf{k}$,
(c) $\mathbf{a} = 3\mathbf{i} - \mathbf{j} - 3\mathbf{k}$, $\mathbf{b} = 2\mathbf{i} + 5\mathbf{j} - 5\mathbf{k}$,
(d) $\mathbf{a} = -5\mathbf{i} - 5\mathbf{j} + 10\mathbf{k}$, $\mathbf{b} = 2\mathbf{i} + 2\mathbf{j} - 3\mathbf{k}$.

1.3 Moments and the vector product

In M1, you found that the moment about a point, O, of a force, F, acting at a point, A, is equal to the force multiplied by the perpendicular distance from O to the line along which the force acts.

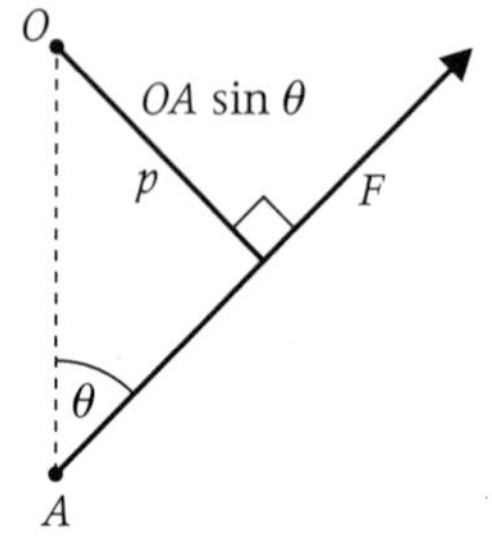

Thus, in the notation shown in the diagram, the moment

$$= F \times p$$
$$= F \times (OA \sin\theta).$$

If $OA = \mathbf{r}$, you will notice that $\mathbf{r} \times \mathbf{F} = rF \sin\theta\, \mathbf{n}$ and hence the magnitude of $\mathbf{r} \times \mathbf{F}$ is $rF \sin\theta$.

> The moment, **M**, of the force is given by
>
> $\mathbf{M} = \mathbf{r} \times \mathbf{F}$

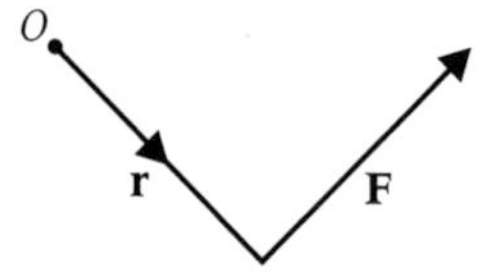

Note that **r** could be the position vector of any point on the line of action of the force; each point will give the same vector moment, **M**.

Worked example 1.12

The force, $\mathbf{F} = 7\mathbf{i} + 2\mathbf{j} - 3\mathbf{k}$ acts through point P with coordinates $(2, -4, 3)$. Find the moment of **F** about Q, a point with coordinates $(3, 3, 5)$.

Solution

In the formula, moment $= \mathbf{r} \times \mathbf{F}$

$$\begin{aligned}
\mathbf{r} &= PQ \\
&= \mathbf{q} - \mathbf{p} \\
&= \begin{pmatrix} 3 \\ 3 \\ 5 \end{pmatrix} - \begin{pmatrix} 2 \\ -4 \\ 3 \end{pmatrix} \\
&= \begin{pmatrix} 1 \\ 7 \\ 2 \end{pmatrix} \\
\text{Moment} &= \begin{pmatrix} 1 \\ 7 \\ 2 \end{pmatrix} \times \begin{pmatrix} 7 \\ 2 \\ -3 \end{pmatrix} \\
&= \begin{vmatrix} \mathbf{i} & \mathbf{j} & \mathbf{k} \\ 1 & 7 & 2 \\ 7 & 2 & -3 \end{vmatrix} \\
&= -25\mathbf{i} + 17\mathbf{j} - 47\mathbf{k}
\end{aligned}$$

Worked example 1.13

Two forces, $\mathbf{F}_1$ and $\mathbf{F}_2$, of magnitudes $3\sqrt{5}$ N and $\sqrt{5}$ N act through the point with position vector $2\mathbf{i} + \mathbf{j}$ in directions $\mathbf{i} + 2\mathbf{j}$ and $\mathbf{i} - 2\mathbf{j}$, respectively. Calculate $\mathbf{F}_1$ and $\mathbf{F}_2$ and hence find $\mathbf{R}$, the resultant of these forces. What is the moment of $\mathbf{R}$ about the origin?

Solution

A unit vector in the direction of $\mathbf{F}_1$ is given by

$$\frac{\mathbf{i} + 2\mathbf{j}}{|\mathbf{i} + 2\mathbf{j}|} = \frac{\mathbf{i} + 2\mathbf{j}}{\sqrt{1^2 + 2^2}} = \frac{\mathbf{i} + 2\mathbf{j}}{\sqrt{5}}.$$

Hence,

$$\begin{aligned}
\mathbf{F}_1 &= 3\sqrt{5}\frac{(\mathbf{i} + 2\mathbf{j})}{\sqrt{5}} \\
&= 3(\mathbf{i} + 2\mathbf{j})
\end{aligned}$$

and, similarly,

$$\begin{aligned}
\mathbf{F}_2 &= \sqrt{5}\frac{(\mathbf{i} - 2\mathbf{j})}{\sqrt{1^2 + 2^2}} \\
&= \mathbf{i} - 2\mathbf{j}
\end{aligned}$$

Hence, $\mathbf{R} = \mathbf{F}_1 + \mathbf{F}_2 = 3(\mathbf{i} + 2\mathbf{j}) + (\mathbf{i} - 2\mathbf{j})$

$$= 4\mathbf{i} + 4\mathbf{j} = 4(\mathbf{i} + \mathbf{j})$$

So the resultant force, $\mathbf{R}$, is in the direction of $\mathbf{i} + \mathbf{j}$ (i.e. parallel to $y = x$).

The magnitude of $\mathbf{R}$ is $\sqrt{4^2 + 4^2} = 4\sqrt{2}$.

Taking moments about the origin gives

$$\mathbf{M} = (2\mathbf{i} + \mathbf{j}) \times 4(\mathbf{i} + \mathbf{j}) = \begin{vmatrix} \mathbf{i} & \mathbf{j} & \mathbf{k} \\ 2 & 1 & 0 \\ 4 & 4 & 0 \end{vmatrix}$$

$$= 4\mathbf{k}$$

Hence $|\mathbf{M}| = 4$, and this must equate to the magnitude of the moment of $\mathbf{R}$ about the origin.

EXERCISE 1C

1 Find the moment, about the origin, of the force $3\mathbf{i} + 6\mathbf{j}$ which acts through the point $(6, -3)$.

2 Find the moment, about the origin, of the force $7\mathbf{i} + 2\mathbf{j}$ which acts through the point $(5, -4)$.

3 Find the moment, about the origin, of the force $5\mathbf{i} - 4\mathbf{j}$ which acts through the point $(-5, -1)$.

4 Find the moment, about the origin, of the force $-7\mathbf{i} + 5\mathbf{j} + 2\mathbf{k}$ which acts through the point $(3, 2, 4)$.

5 Find the moment, about the point $(2, -1)$, of the force $2\mathbf{i} + 7\mathbf{j}$ which acts through the point $(3, -2)$.

6 Find the moment, about the point $(4, -3, 1)$, of the force $5\mathbf{i} + 10\mathbf{j} - 5\mathbf{k}$ which acts through the point $(-5, 7, 1)$.

7 Find the moment, about the point $(12, -1)$, of the force $-7\mathbf{i} - 3\mathbf{j}$ which acts through the point $(4, -8)$.

8 Find the moment, about the point $(1, 3, 2)$, of the force $5\mathbf{i} + 4\mathbf{j} + 2\mathbf{k}$ which acts through the point $(-1, -6, 4)$.

1.4 Reduction of a system of forces

As we found in M4, two or more systems of **coplanar** forces, which produce exactly the same linear and turning effects on a rigid body are called **equivalent systems of forces**.

> When you are using vector techniques, systems of coplanar forces are equivalent if and only if:
>
> **(a)** the vector sums of the two force systems are equal,
>
> **(b)** the resulting moment about any point in the plane containing the forces is identical in both systems.
>
> Both of these conditions need to be satisfied if the two force systems are to be equivalent.

A system of **coplanar** forces can always be reduced to a **single force** provided that the resultant of the coplanar forces is non-zero.

Worked example 1.14

Show that the two force systems, illustrated below, are equivalent.

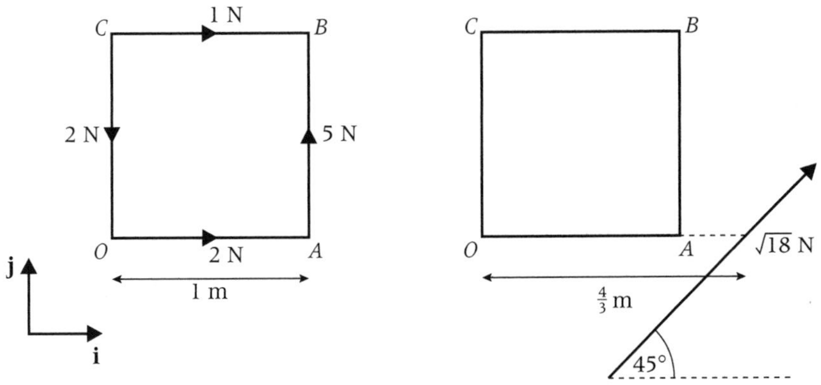

Solution

Using a vector approach (although there is no need in this example) you can write, for the first system,

$$\begin{aligned}
\mathbf{F}_1 &= 2\mathbf{i}, & \mathbf{r}_1 &= \mathbf{0}\\
\mathbf{F}_2 &= 5\mathbf{j}, & \mathbf{r}_2 &= \mathbf{i}\\
\mathbf{F}_3 &= \mathbf{i}, & \mathbf{r}_3 &= \mathbf{j}\\
\mathbf{F}_4 &= -2\mathbf{j}, & \mathbf{r}_4 &= \mathbf{0}
\end{aligned}$$

Here $\mathbf{r}_i$ are points on the line of action of the force $\mathbf{F}_i$.

For the second system,

$$\mathbf{R} = \frac{\sqrt{18}(\mathbf{i}+\mathbf{j})}{\sqrt{2}} = 3\mathbf{i} + 3\mathbf{j}, \quad \mathbf{r} = \frac{4}{3}\mathbf{i}$$

Thus $$\begin{aligned}\mathbf{F}_1 + \mathbf{F}_2 + \mathbf{F}_3 + \mathbf{F}_4 &= 2\mathbf{i} + 5\mathbf{j} + \mathbf{i} - 2\mathbf{j}\\ &= 3\mathbf{i} + 3\mathbf{j}\\ &= \mathbf{R}\end{aligned}$$

satisfying condition **(a)**.

Similarly,

$$\begin{aligned}&\mathbf{r}_1 \times \mathbf{F}_1 + \mathbf{r}_2 \times \mathbf{F}_2 + \mathbf{r}_3 \times \mathbf{F}_3 + \mathbf{r}_4 \times \mathbf{F}_4\\ &\quad= (\mathbf{0} \times 2\mathbf{i}) + (\mathbf{i} \times 5\mathbf{j}) + (\mathbf{j} \times \mathbf{i}) + (\mathbf{0} \times (-2\mathbf{j}))\\ &\quad= 5\mathbf{k} - \mathbf{k}\\ &\quad= 4\mathbf{k}\end{aligned}$$

and $$\begin{aligned}\mathbf{r} \times \mathbf{R} &= \frac{4}{3}\mathbf{i} \times (3\mathbf{i} + 3\mathbf{j})\\ &= 4\mathbf{k}\end{aligned}$$

Condition **(b)** is satisfied and the two systems of forces are equivalent.

Worked example 1.15

OABC is a square of side 1 m, with forces acting along the sides as shown opposite.

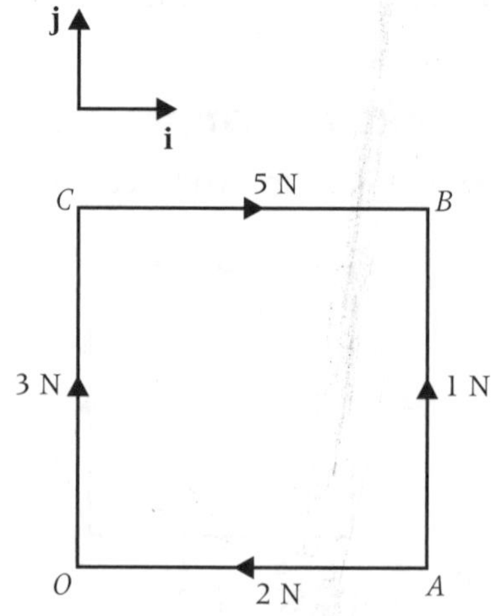

Calculate:

(a) the resultant force,

(b) the moment of these forces about *O*,

(c) the distance from *O* of the point where the line of action of the resultant force cuts *OA*.

Solution

(a) With the usual notation

$$\mathbf{F}_1 = -2\mathbf{i}, \quad \mathbf{r}_1 = \mathbf{0} \quad (\mathbf{r}_1 \text{ is a point on the line of action of } \mathbf{F}_1)$$

$$\mathbf{F}_2 = \mathbf{j}, \quad \mathbf{r}_2 = \mathbf{i}$$

$$\mathbf{F}_3 = 5\mathbf{i}, \quad \mathbf{r}_3 = \mathbf{j}$$

$$\mathbf{F}_4 = 3\mathbf{j}, \quad \mathbf{r}_4 = \mathbf{0}$$

So $\mathbf{R} = \mathbf{F}_1 + \mathbf{F}_2 + \mathbf{F}_3 + \mathbf{F}_4$

$$= -2\mathbf{i} + \mathbf{j} + 5\mathbf{i} + 3\mathbf{j}$$

$$= 3\mathbf{i} + 4\mathbf{j}$$

(b) $\mathbf{M} = \mathbf{r}_1 \times \mathbf{F}_1 + \mathbf{r}_2 \times \mathbf{F}_2 + \mathbf{r}_3 \times \mathbf{F}_3 + \mathbf{r}_4 \times \mathbf{F}_4$

$$= \mathbf{0}(-2\mathbf{i}) + \mathbf{i} \times \mathbf{j} + \mathbf{j} \times 5\mathbf{i} + \mathbf{0} \times 3\mathbf{j}$$

$$= \mathbf{k} - 5\mathbf{k}$$

$$= -4\mathbf{k}$$

(c) If d is the perpendicular distance of the line of action of $\mathbf{R}$ from the point O, then

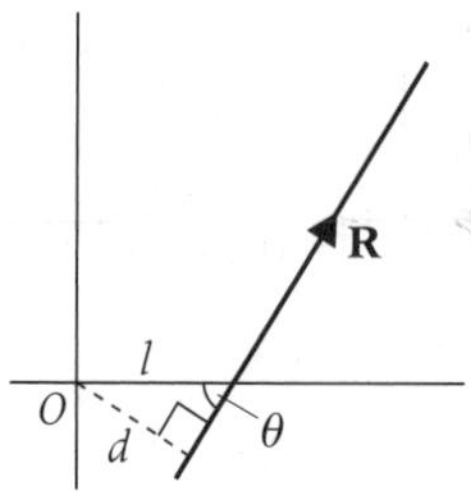

$$l = \frac{d}{\sin\theta}, \text{ where } \sin\theta = \frac{4}{5} \quad \left(\text{since } \tan\theta = \frac{4}{3}\right)$$

and from **(b)** above

$$-4 = |\mathbf{R}|d = 5d$$

Hence,

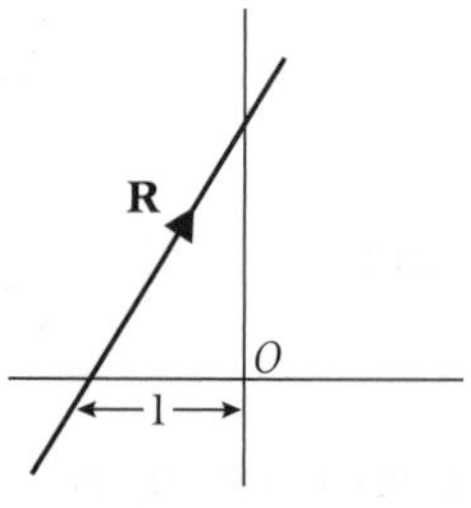

$$l = \frac{5d}{4} = \frac{5}{4}\left(-\frac{4}{5}\right) = -1$$

the negative sign indicating that it is on the negative x-axis as shown opposite.

Worked example 1.16

Forces $2P$, $3P$ and $4P$ act along the sides $\overrightarrow{OA}$, $\overrightarrow{AB}$ and $\overrightarrow{BO}$ of an equilateral triangle OAB of side of length a. Find:

(a) the resultant force,

(b) the distance from O of the point where it cuts OB.

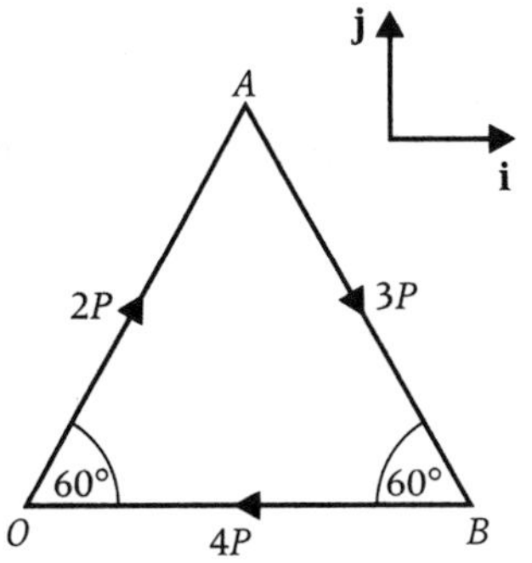

Solution

(a) In vector terms

$$\mathbf{F}_1 = 2P\cos 60°\mathbf{i} + 2P\sin 60°\mathbf{j} = P\mathbf{i} + \sqrt{3}P\mathbf{j}$$

$$\mathbf{F}_2 = 3P\cos 60°\mathbf{i} - 3P\sin 60°\mathbf{j} = \frac{3}{2}P\mathbf{i} - \frac{3\sqrt{3}}{2}P\mathbf{j}$$

$$\mathbf{F}_3 = -4P\mathbf{i}$$

So the resultant force is given by

$$\begin{aligned}\mathbf{R} &= \mathbf{F}_1 + \mathbf{F}_2 + \mathbf{F}_3 \\ &= P\mathbf{i} + \sqrt{3}P\mathbf{j} + \frac{3}{2}P\mathbf{i} - \frac{3\sqrt{3}}{2}P\mathbf{j} - 4P\mathbf{i} \\ &= -\frac{3}{2}P\mathbf{i} - \frac{\sqrt{3}}{2}P\mathbf{j}\end{aligned}$$

Its magnitude is given by

$$|\mathbf{R}| = P\sqrt{\frac{9}{4} + \frac{3}{4}} = \sqrt{3}P$$

and its direction is given by

$$\tan\theta = \left(\frac{\frac{\sqrt{3}}{2}}{\frac{3}{2}}\right) = \frac{1}{\sqrt{3}}$$

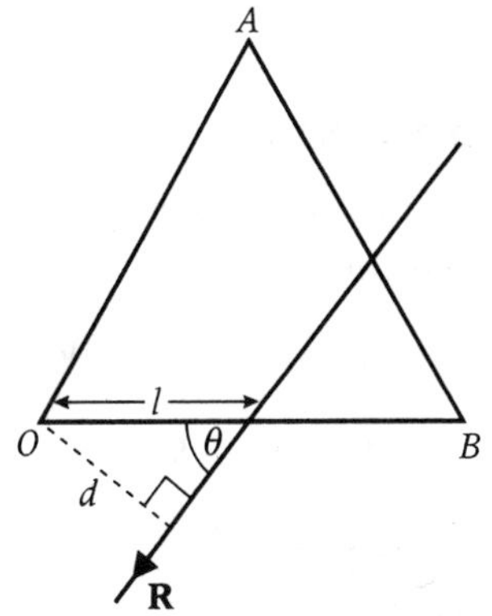

where θ is as shown in the diagram opposite.

Thus $\theta = 30°$.

(b) If d is the perpendicular distance of the line of action of $\mathbf{R}$ from the origin, then

$$d|\mathbf{R}| = P\sqrt{3}d$$

must equal the clockwise magnitude of the moment of the three forces about O. This moment is given by

$$\begin{aligned}\mathbf{M} &= \mathbf{0} \times \mathbf{F}_1 + \overrightarrow{OB} \times \mathbf{F}_2 + \mathbf{0} \times \mathbf{F}_3 \\ &= a\mathbf{i} \times \left(\frac{3}{2}P\mathbf{i} - \frac{3\sqrt{3}}{2}P\mathbf{j}\right) \\ &= -\frac{3\sqrt{3}}{2}aP\mathbf{k}\end{aligned}$$

From the diagram, $\mathbf{R}$ crosses OB at the point $(l, 0, 0)$

$$\text{Moment of } \mathbf{R} \text{ about } O \text{ is } \mathbf{r}\times\mathbf{F} = \begin{vmatrix} \mathbf{i} & \mathbf{j} & \mathbf{k} \\ l & 0 & 0 \\ -\frac{3}{2}p & -\frac{\sqrt{3}}{2}p & 0 \end{vmatrix}$$

$$= -\frac{\sqrt{3}}{2}pl\mathbf{k}$$

$$\text{Since} \quad \mathbf{M} = -\frac{3\sqrt{3}}{2}ap\mathbf{k}$$

$$-\frac{3\sqrt{3}}{2}ap\mathbf{k} = -\frac{\sqrt{3}}{2}pl\mathbf{k}$$

Hence, the distance from O of the point where it cuts OB is $3a$.

Worked example 1.17

Find the force, $\mathbf{F}$, and its line of action, which is equivalent to the forces $\mathbf{F}_1 = 3\mathbf{i} - 2\mathbf{j}$ acting at A (4, 1), $\mathbf{F}_2 = 2\mathbf{i} + 7\mathbf{j}$ acting at B (3, 2), and $\mathbf{F}_3 = 4\mathbf{i} + 5\mathbf{j}$ acting at C (−3, 5).

Solution

A similar problem in M4 was solved, by considering the separate components of the forces, acting in the x and y directions.

Using a vector approach,

$$\mathbf{F} = \mathbf{F}_1 + \mathbf{F}_2 + \mathbf{F}_3$$

$$= \begin{pmatrix} 3 \\ -2 \end{pmatrix} + \begin{pmatrix} 2 \\ 7 \end{pmatrix} + \begin{pmatrix} 4 \\ 5 \end{pmatrix} = \begin{pmatrix} 9 \\ 10 \end{pmatrix}$$

The moment of $\mathbf{F}$ about O (0, 0) is the same as the sum of the moments of $\mathbf{F}_1$, $\mathbf{F}_2$ and $\mathbf{F}_3$ about O.

$$\text{The moment of } \mathbf{F}_1 \text{ about } O \text{ is } \begin{vmatrix} \mathbf{i} & \mathbf{j} & \mathbf{k} \\ 4 & 1 & 0 \\ 3 & -2 & 0 \end{vmatrix} = -11\mathbf{k}.$$

(Note that for $\mathbf{F}_1$, $\mathbf{r} = \overrightarrow{OA} = 4\mathbf{i} + \mathbf{j}$.)

$$\text{Similarly, the moment of } \mathbf{F}_2 \text{ about } O \text{ is } \begin{vmatrix} \mathbf{i} & \mathbf{j} & \mathbf{k} \\ 3 & 2 & 0 \\ 2 & 7 & 0 \end{vmatrix} = 17\mathbf{k}.$$

And the moment of $\mathbf{F}_3$ about O is $\begin{vmatrix} \mathbf{i} & \mathbf{j} & \mathbf{k} \\ -3 & 5 & 0 \\ 4 & 5 & 0 \end{vmatrix} = -35\mathbf{k}$.

The total moment of $\mathbf{F}_1$, $\mathbf{F}_2$ and $\mathbf{F}_3$ is
$-11\mathbf{k} + 17\mathbf{k} - 35\mathbf{k} = -29\mathbf{k}$.

Let the equivalent force $\mathbf{F}$ act through the point $(a, 0)$.

Moment of force $\mathbf{F}$ is $\begin{vmatrix} \mathbf{i} & \mathbf{j} & \mathbf{k} \\ a & 0 & 0 \\ 9 & 10 & 0 \end{vmatrix} = 10a\mathbf{k}$.

$$10a\mathbf{k} = -29\mathbf{k}$$

$$a = -2.9$$

The equivalent force is $9\mathbf{i} + 10\mathbf{j}$ and its line of action is

$$\mathbf{r} = \begin{pmatrix} -2.9 \\ 0 \end{pmatrix} + t\begin{pmatrix} 9 \\ 10 \end{pmatrix}.$$

Worked example 1.18

Find the force, $\mathbf{F}$, which is equivalent to the forces $\mathbf{F}_1$ and $\mathbf{F}_2$, and the point where its line of action crosses the line $y = 2x$. The force $\mathbf{F}_1 = 5\mathbf{i} + 6\mathbf{j}$ acts at the point A (2, 3) and the force $\mathbf{F}_2 = 3\mathbf{i} - 5\mathbf{j}$ acts at the point B (6, 9).

Solution

First find the resultant of the two forces

$$\mathbf{F} = \mathbf{F}_1 + \mathbf{F}_2$$

$$= \begin{pmatrix} 5 \\ 6 \end{pmatrix} + \begin{pmatrix} 3 \\ -5 \end{pmatrix} = \begin{pmatrix} 8 \\ 1 \end{pmatrix}$$

The moment of $\mathbf{F}$ about O (0, 0) is the same as the sum of the moments of $\mathbf{F}_1$ and $\mathbf{F}_2$ about O.
Using $\mathbf{r} \times \mathbf{F}$, the moment of $\mathbf{F}_1$ about O is

$$\begin{vmatrix} \mathbf{i} & \mathbf{j} & \mathbf{k} \\ 2 & 3 & 0 \\ 5 & 6 & 0 \end{vmatrix} = -3\mathbf{k}.$$

Similarly, the moment of $\mathbf{F}_2$ about O is

$$\begin{vmatrix} \mathbf{i} & \mathbf{j} & \mathbf{k} \\ 6 & 9 & 0 \\ 3 & -5 & 0 \end{vmatrix} = -57\mathbf{k}.$$

The total moment of $\mathbf{F}_1$ and $\mathbf{F}_2$ is

$$-3\mathbf{k} - 57\mathbf{k} = -60\mathbf{k}.$$

You require the point where the line of action of **F** crosses the line $y = 2x$.
The general point on the line $y = 2x$ is $(t, 2t)$.
Hence, let the equivalent force **F** act through the point $(t, 2t)$.
Moment of force **F** is

$$\begin{vmatrix} \mathbf{i} & \mathbf{j} & \mathbf{k} \\ t & 2t & 0 \\ 8 & 1 & 0 \end{vmatrix} = -15t\mathbf{k}.$$

As the two moments calculated must be equal

$$-60\mathbf{k} = -15t\mathbf{k}$$
$$t = 4$$

The equivalent force is $8\mathbf{i} + 1\mathbf{j}$ and its line of action crosses the line $y = 2x$ at the point $(4, 8)$.

Reduction of a system of forces to a couple

A system of **coplanar** forces reduces to a couple if both of the following conditions are satisfied:

(a) the resultant force is zero,

(b) the resultant moment about any point in the plane is non-zero.

An alternative condition is that the resultant moment about any three non-colinear points is non-zero.

Worked example 1.19

Show that the system of forces shown opposite is equivalent to a couple. Find its moment. (The square is of side 1 m.)

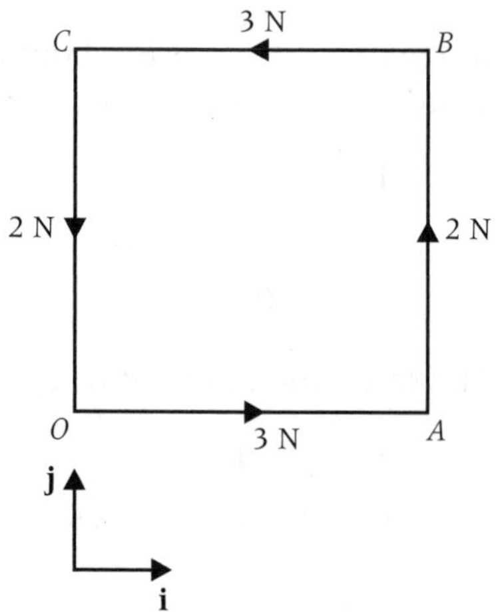

Solution

Clearly $\mathbf{R} = 3\mathbf{i} + 2\mathbf{j} - 3\mathbf{i} - 2\mathbf{j} = \mathbf{0}$ so the resultant force is zero.

Taking moments about O,

$$\mathbf{M} = (\mathbf{0} \times 3\mathbf{i}) + (\mathbf{i} \times 2\mathbf{j}) + (\mathbf{j} \times (-3\mathbf{i})) + (\mathbf{0} \times (-2\mathbf{j}))$$
$$= 2\mathbf{k} + 3\mathbf{k} = 5\mathbf{k}$$

Hence the system of forces is equivalent to a couple of moment 5 N m.

Worked example 1.20

ABC is an isosceles triangle with $AB = AC = 10$ cm, and $BC = 12$ cm. M is the midpoint of BC. Forces act as shown in the diagram. Show that this system of forces is equivalent to a couple.

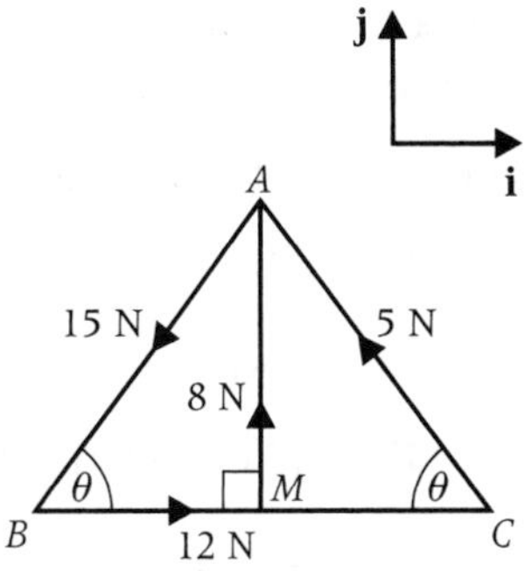

Solution

The forces can be written, in vector form, as

$$\mathbf{F}_1 = 12\mathbf{i}$$
$$\mathbf{F}_2 = 8\mathbf{j}$$
$$\mathbf{F}_3 = -5\cos\theta\mathbf{i} + 5\sin\theta\mathbf{j}$$
$$\mathbf{F}_4 = -15\cos\theta\mathbf{i} - 15\sin\theta\mathbf{j}$$

where $\cos\theta = \frac{3}{5}, \quad \sin\theta = \frac{4}{5}$

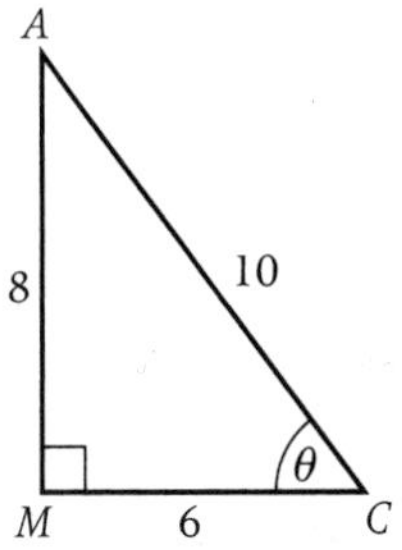

Hence, $\mathbf{F}_1 = 12\mathbf{i}$, $\mathbf{F}_2 = 8\mathbf{j}$, $\mathbf{F}_3 = -3\mathbf{i} + 4\mathbf{j}$, $\mathbf{F}_4 = -9\mathbf{i} - 12\mathbf{j}$

and
$$\begin{aligned}\mathbf{R} &= \mathbf{F}_1 + \mathbf{F}_2 + \mathbf{F}_3 + \mathbf{F}_4 \\ &= 12\mathbf{i} + 8\mathbf{j} + (-3\mathbf{i} + 4\mathbf{j}) + (-9\mathbf{i} - 12\mathbf{j}) \\ &= \mathbf{0}\end{aligned}$$

so that the resultant force is zero.

The moment of the couple is given by (since $\mathbf{r}_2 = 0.06\mathbf{i}$, etc.)

$$\begin{aligned}\mathbf{M} &= \mathbf{0} \times \mathbf{F}_1 + \left(\frac{6}{100}\mathbf{i}\right) \times 8\mathbf{j} + \left(\frac{12}{100}\mathbf{i}\right) \times (-3\mathbf{i} + 4\mathbf{j}) + \mathbf{0} \times \mathbf{F}_4 \\ &= 0.48\mathbf{k} + 0.48\mathbf{k} \\ &= 0.96\mathbf{k}\end{aligned}$$

and its magnitude is 0.96 N m.

Any system of coplanar forces acting on a rigid body may be replaced by an equivalent system consisting of a single force, acting at a particular point in the plane of the forces, together with a couple.

Worked example 1.21

Forces act along the sides of an equilateral triangle, of side of length a, as shown opposite. A force of 2 N acts along BC. Find the force at O and the couple which together are equivalent to this system.

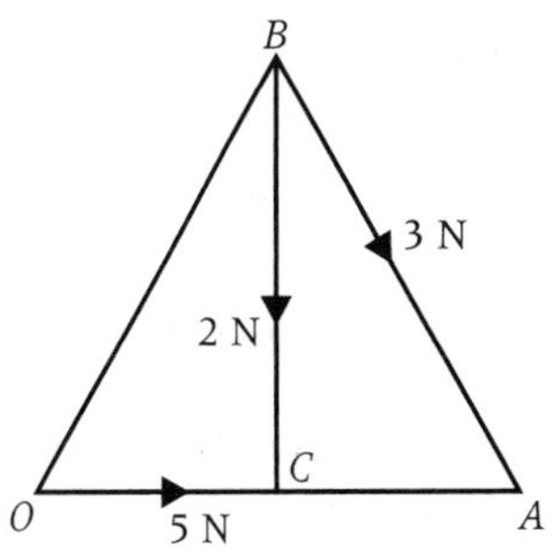

Solution

Let **R** be the single force, at angle θ to OA, and **G** be the anticlockwise moment of the couple.

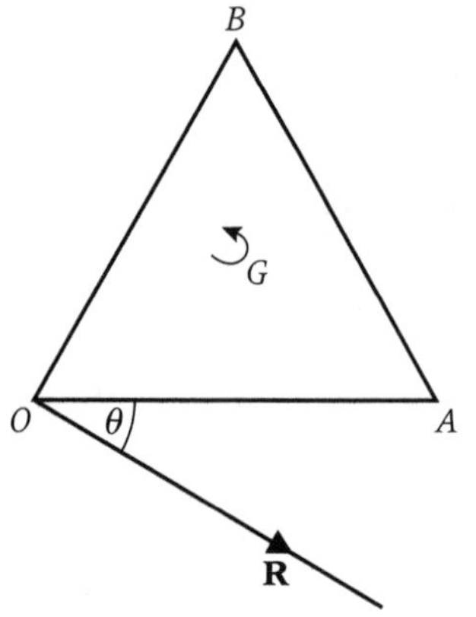

Then, in vector notation,

$$\mathbf{F}_1 = 5\mathbf{i}, \qquad \mathbf{r}_1 = \mathbf{0}$$

$$\mathbf{F}_2 = -2\mathbf{j}, \qquad \mathbf{r}_2 = \frac{a}{2}\mathbf{i}$$

$$\mathbf{F}_3 = (3\cos 60°)\mathbf{i} - (3\sin 60°)\mathbf{j}, \quad \mathbf{r}_3 = a\mathbf{i}$$

Hence, $\mathbf{R} = \mathbf{F}_1 + \mathbf{F}_2 + \mathbf{F}_3$

$$= 5\mathbf{i} - 2\mathbf{j} + \frac{3}{2}\mathbf{i} - \frac{3\sqrt{3}}{2}\mathbf{j}$$

$$= \frac{13}{2}\mathbf{i} - \frac{(4+3\sqrt{3})}{2}\mathbf{j}$$

giving $|\mathbf{R}| = \left(\frac{169}{4} + \frac{(4+3\sqrt{3})^2}{4}\right)^{\frac{1}{2}} \approx 7.96\text{ N}$

and $\tan\theta = \left(\frac{4+3\sqrt{3}}{13}\right) \Rightarrow \theta \approx 35.3°.$

Moments about O give

$$\mathbf{M} = \mathbf{0} \times \mathbf{F}_1 + \frac{a}{2}\mathbf{i} \times (-2\mathbf{j}) + a\mathbf{i} \times \left(\frac{3}{2}\mathbf{i} - \frac{3\sqrt{3}}{2}\mathbf{j}\right)$$

$$= -a\mathbf{k} - a\frac{3\sqrt{3}}{2}\mathbf{k}$$

$$= -a\frac{(2+3\sqrt{3})}{2}\mathbf{k}$$

Thus, the couple has a clockwise moment of magnitude

$$a\frac{(2+3\sqrt{3})}{2}\text{ N m.}$$

Worked example 1.22

A rectangular lamina has consecutive vertices A, B, C and D whose position vectors with respect to a given origin, O, are $2\mathbf{i} + 5\mathbf{j}$, $5\mathbf{i} + 9\mathbf{j}$, $-3\mathbf{i} + 15\mathbf{j}$ and $-6\mathbf{i} + 11\mathbf{j}$, respectively, where **i** and **j** are perpendicular unit vectors. Forces represented in magnitude, direction and line of action by

$$p\overrightarrow{AB},\ q\overrightarrow{BC},\ r\overrightarrow{CD} \text{ and } \overrightarrow{DA}$$

act on the lamina.

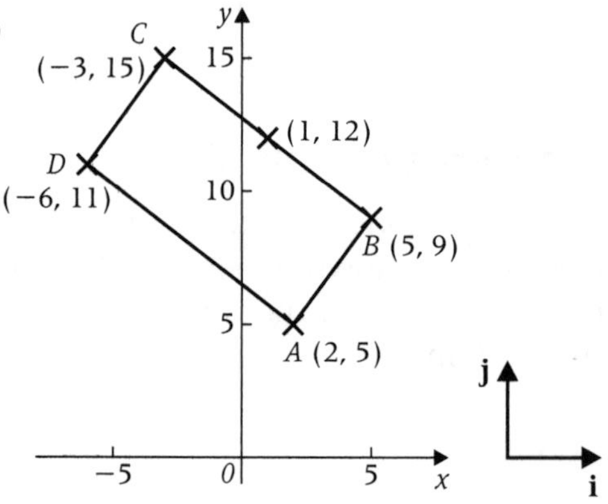

(a) Express the above forces in the form $a\mathbf{i} + b\mathbf{j}$ and hence express their resultant in this form.

(b) Show that the magnitude of the moment of these forces about A is $|50q + 50r|$.

(i) Given that the lamina is in equilibrium, find p, q and r.

(ii) Given that the lamina is **not** in equilibrium and that the resultant force passes through the midpoint of BC, show that $p + r + 2 = 0$.

Solution

(a) $\mathbf{F}_1 = p\overrightarrow{AB} = p(3\mathbf{i} + 4\mathbf{j})$

$\mathbf{F}_2 = q\overrightarrow{BC} = q(-8\mathbf{i} + 6\mathbf{j})$

$\mathbf{F}_3 = r\overrightarrow{CD} = r(-3\mathbf{i} - 4\mathbf{j})$

$\mathbf{F}_4 = \overrightarrow{DA} = 8\mathbf{i} - 6\mathbf{j}$

$$\begin{aligned}\mathbf{R} &= \mathbf{F}_1 + \mathbf{F}_2 + \mathbf{F}_3 + \mathbf{F}_4\\ &= p(3\mathbf{i} + 4\mathbf{j}) + q(-8\mathbf{i} + 6\mathbf{j}) + r(-3\mathbf{i} - 4\mathbf{j}) + 8\mathbf{i} - 6\mathbf{j}\\ &= (3p - 8q - 3r + 8)\mathbf{i} + (4p + 6q - 4r - 6)\mathbf{j}\end{aligned}$$

(b) To find the moment about the point A, you require the position vector relative to A of a point on the line of each force. For example

$$\mathbf{r}_1 = \mathbf{0},\ \mathbf{r}_2 = \overrightarrow{AB} = 3\mathbf{i} + 4\mathbf{j},\ \mathbf{r}_3 = \overrightarrow{AD} = -8\mathbf{i} + 6\mathbf{j},\ \mathbf{r}_4 = \mathbf{0}$$

giving

$$\begin{aligned}\mathbf{M}_A &= \mathbf{0} \times \mathbf{F}_1 + (3\mathbf{i} + 4\mathbf{j}) \times q(-8\mathbf{i} + 6\mathbf{j}) + (-8\mathbf{i} + 6\mathbf{j}) \times r(-3\mathbf{i} - 4\mathbf{j}) + \mathbf{0} \times \mathbf{F}_4\\ &= q(18\mathbf{k} + 32\mathbf{k}) + r(32\mathbf{k} + 18\mathbf{k})\\ &= (50q + 50r)\mathbf{k}.\end{aligned}$$

Hence,

$$|\mathbf{M}_A| = |50q + 50r|$$

(i) If the lamina is in equilibrium

$$\mathbf{R} = \mathbf{F}_1 + \mathbf{F}_2 + \mathbf{F}_3 + \mathbf{F}_4 = \mathbf{0}$$

and $\mathbf{M}_A = \mathbf{0}$.

This gives

$$p(3\mathbf{i} + 4\mathbf{j}) + q(-8\mathbf{i} + 6\mathbf{j}) + r(-3\mathbf{i} - 4\mathbf{j}) + 8\mathbf{i} - 6\mathbf{j} = \mathbf{0}$$

$$[\mathbf{i}] : 3p - 8q - 3r + 8 = 0$$

$$[\mathbf{j}] : 4p + 6q - 4r - 6 = 0$$

and

$$50q + 50r = 0 \Rightarrow q + r = 0.$$

Substituting $q = -r$ in the first two equations gives

$$\left.\begin{aligned}3p + 5r &= -8\\ 4p - 10r &= 6\end{aligned}\right\} 5p = -5.$$

Thus $p = -1$, $r = -1$ and $q = 1$.

(ii) The resultant force, $\mathbf{R}_1$, passes through the point with coordinates (1, 12) and position vector, relative to A, $-\mathbf{i} + 7\mathbf{j}$.

Hence the moment of $\mathbf{R}_1$ about A is given by

$$\begin{aligned}\mathbf{M}_A &= (-\mathbf{i} + 7\mathbf{j}) \times \{(3p - 8q - 3r + 8)\mathbf{i} + (4p + 6q - 4r - 6)\mathbf{j}\} \\ &= (-4p - 6q + 4r + 6)\mathbf{k} - 7(3p - 8q - 3r + 8)\mathbf{k} \\ &= (-25p + 50q + 25r - 50)\mathbf{k}\end{aligned}$$

From above, this must equal $(50q + 50r)\mathbf{k}$.

Hence,

$$\begin{aligned}-25p - 25r - 50 &= 0 \\ \Rightarrow \qquad p + r + 2 &= 0\end{aligned}$$

Forces in three dimensions

The above techniques can be extended to three-dimensional problems.

> Three or more forces can always be made equivalent to a force which passes through any chosen point together with a couple.
> A couple and a force cannot, in three dimensions, normally be combined into one force.

Worked example 1.23

Find the force, $\mathbf{F}$, acting through O which together with a couple, $\mathbf{G}$, is equivalent to the forces $\mathbf{F}_1$, $\mathbf{F}_2$, $\mathbf{F}_3$, where:

$\mathbf{F}_1 = 2\mathbf{i} - 3\mathbf{j} + 7\mathbf{k}$ acting at $A(2, 3, -4)$

$\mathbf{F}_2 = 4\mathbf{i} + 2\mathbf{j} - 3\mathbf{k}$ acting at $B(-1, 2, 5)$

$\mathbf{F}_3 = -\mathbf{i} + 4\mathbf{j} - 2\mathbf{k}$ acting at $C(3, 4, 7)$

Solution

First find the resultant of the three forces.

$$\mathbf{F} = \mathbf{F}_1 + \mathbf{F}_2 + \mathbf{F}_3 = \begin{pmatrix} 2 \\ -3 \\ 7 \end{pmatrix} + \begin{pmatrix} 4 \\ 2 \\ -3 \end{pmatrix} + \begin{pmatrix} -1 \\ 4 \\ -2 \end{pmatrix} = \begin{pmatrix} 5 \\ 3 \\ 2 \end{pmatrix}$$

The moment of $\mathbf{F}_1$ about O is given by,

$$\begin{vmatrix} \mathbf{i} & \mathbf{j} & \mathbf{k} \\ 2 & 3 & -4 \\ 2 & -3 & 7 \end{vmatrix} = 9\mathbf{i} - 22\mathbf{j} - 12\mathbf{k}.$$

The moment of $\mathbf{F}_2$ about O is given by,

$$\begin{vmatrix} \mathbf{i} & \mathbf{j} & \mathbf{k} \\ -1 & 2 & 5 \\ 4 & 2 & -3 \end{vmatrix} = -16\mathbf{i} + 17\mathbf{j} - 10\mathbf{k}.$$

The moment of $\mathbf{F}_3$ about O is given by,

$$\begin{vmatrix} \mathbf{i} & \mathbf{j} & \mathbf{k} \\ 3 & 4 & 7 \\ -1 & 4 & -2 \end{vmatrix} = -36\mathbf{i} - \mathbf{j} + 16\mathbf{k}.$$

The total moment of $\mathbf{F}_1$, $\mathbf{F}_2$, $\mathbf{F}_3$ about O is

$$(9\mathbf{i} - 22\mathbf{j} - 12\mathbf{k}) + (-16\mathbf{i} + 17\mathbf{j} - 10\mathbf{k}) + (-36\mathbf{i} - \mathbf{j} + 16\mathbf{k})$$
$$= -43\mathbf{i} - 6\mathbf{j} - 6\mathbf{k}$$

So the three forces, $\mathbf{F}_1$, $\mathbf{F}_2$, $\mathbf{F}_3$, are equivalent to a single force $5\mathbf{i} + 3\mathbf{i} + 2\mathbf{k}$ acting at O together with a couple, $\mathbf{G} = -43\mathbf{i} - 6\mathbf{j} - 6\mathbf{k}$.

Note that the magnitude of the couple is

$$\sqrt{43^2 + 6^2 + 6^2} = \sqrt{1921}.$$

Worked example 1.24

Three forces, $\mathbf{F}_1$, $\mathbf{F}_2$ and $\mathbf{F}_3$, act on a rigid body at points A, B and C, with position vectors $\mathbf{r}_1$, $\mathbf{r}_2$ and $\mathbf{r}_3$, respectively, relative to an origin O, where

$$\mathbf{F}_1 = \mathbf{i} - \mathbf{j} + 2\mathbf{k}, \quad \mathbf{r}_1 = 3\mathbf{i} - \mathbf{j} + \mathbf{k}$$
$$\mathbf{F}_2 = \mathbf{i} + 3\mathbf{j} - \mathbf{k}, \quad \mathbf{r}_2 = \mathbf{j} + 2\mathbf{k}$$
$$\mathbf{F}_3 = \alpha\mathbf{i} + \beta\mathbf{j} + 2\mathbf{k}, \quad \mathbf{r}_3 = \mathbf{k}$$

and α and β are constants.

Find:

(a) the shortest distance from the point B, with position vector $\mathbf{r}_2$, to the line of action of the force $\mathbf{F}_1$

(b) the single force $\mathbf{F}$ acting at O and the couple $\mathbf{G}$ to which the system of forces $\mathbf{F}_1$, $\mathbf{F}_2$ and $\mathbf{F}_3$ reduces.

Determine α and β such that $\mathbf{G}$ is parallel to $\mathbf{F}$.

Solution

(a) The magnitude of the moment of the force $\mathbf{F}_1$ about the point B with position vector $\mathbf{r}_2$ is equal to the product of the magnitude of the force $\mathbf{F}_1$ and the perpendicular distance from B to the line of action of $\mathbf{F}_1$.

$$\overrightarrow{BA} = \mathbf{r}_1 - \mathbf{r}_2 = 3\mathbf{i} - 2\mathbf{j} - \mathbf{k}$$

Moment of the force $\mathbf{F}_1$ about B is

$$\overrightarrow{BA} \times \mathbf{F}_1 = \begin{vmatrix} \mathbf{i} & \mathbf{j} & \mathbf{k} \\ 3 & -2 & -1 \\ 1 & -1 & 2 \end{vmatrix}$$

$$= -5\mathbf{i} - 7\mathbf{j} - \mathbf{k}$$

$$\therefore \quad |\overrightarrow{BA} \times \mathbf{F}_1| = \sqrt{(-5)^2 + (-7)^2 + (-1)^2}$$

$$= \sqrt{75}$$

$$= 5\sqrt{3}$$

$$\text{Magnitude of } \mathbf{F}_1 = \sqrt{1^2 + (-1)^2 + 2^2}$$

$$= \sqrt{6}$$

The shortest distance, which is the perpendicular distance,

is $\dfrac{5\sqrt{3}}{\sqrt{6}} = \dfrac{5}{\sqrt{2}}$ or $\dfrac{5\sqrt{2}}{2}$.

(b) The single force $\mathbf{F}$ is given by

$$\mathbf{F} = \mathbf{F}_1 + \mathbf{F}_2 + \mathbf{F}_3$$

$$= (\mathbf{i} - \mathbf{j} + 2\mathbf{k}) + (\mathbf{i} + 3\mathbf{j} - \mathbf{k}) + (\alpha\mathbf{i} + \beta\mathbf{j} + 2\mathbf{k})$$

$$= (2 + \alpha)\mathbf{i} + (2 + \beta)\mathbf{j} + 3\mathbf{k}$$

The moment of the forces about O is given by

$$\sum_{i=1}^{3} \mathbf{r}_i \times \mathbf{F}_i = \begin{vmatrix} \mathbf{i} & \mathbf{j} & \mathbf{k} \\ 3 & -1 & 1 \\ 1 & -1 & 2 \end{vmatrix} + \begin{vmatrix} \mathbf{i} & \mathbf{j} & \mathbf{k} \\ 0 & 1 & 2 \\ 1 & 3 & -1 \end{vmatrix} + \begin{vmatrix} \mathbf{i} & \mathbf{j} & \mathbf{k} \\ 0 & 0 & 1 \\ \alpha & \beta & 2 \end{vmatrix}$$

$$= (-\mathbf{i} - 5\mathbf{j} - 2\mathbf{k}) + (-7\mathbf{i} + 2\mathbf{j} - \mathbf{k}) + (-\beta\mathbf{i} + \alpha\mathbf{j})$$

$$= (-8 - \beta)\mathbf{i} + (-3 + \alpha)\mathbf{j} - 3\mathbf{k}$$

To balance this, a couple $\mathbf{G}$ is required, where

$$\mathbf{G} = (8 + \beta)\mathbf{i} + (3 - \alpha)\mathbf{j} + 3\mathbf{k}$$

$$\text{so} \quad |\mathbf{G}| = \left[(8 + \beta)^2 + (3 - \alpha)^2 + 9\right]^{\frac{1}{2}}$$

The vectors $\mathbf{G}$ and $\mathbf{F}$ are parallel, since the $\mathbf{k}$ components are equal, provided

$$\left.\begin{aligned} 8 + \beta &= 2 + \alpha \\ 3 - \alpha &= 2 + \beta \end{aligned}\right\} \alpha = \frac{7}{2}, \ \beta = -\frac{5}{2}$$

EXERCISE 1D

1 Find the force, $\mathbf{F}$, and its line of action, which is equivalent to the forces $\mathbf{F}_1 = 5\mathbf{i} - 4\mathbf{j}$ acting at $A\ (-2, 5)$, $\mathbf{F}_2 = 3\mathbf{i} + 4\mathbf{j}$ acting at $B\ (4, -1)$ and $\mathbf{F}_3 = 11\mathbf{i} + 5\mathbf{j}$ acting at $C\ (7, 11)$.

2 Find the force, $\mathbf{F}$, and its line of action, which is equivalent to the forces $\mathbf{F}_1 = 4\mathbf{i} + 2\mathbf{j}$ acting at $A\ (5, 4)$, $\mathbf{F}_2 = 2\mathbf{i} + 7\mathbf{j}$ acting at $B\ (3, -7)$ and $\mathbf{F}_3 = 7\mathbf{i} - 4\mathbf{j}$ acting at $C\ (-3, 6)$.

3 Find the force, $\mathbf{F}$, and its line of action, which is equivalent to the forces $\mathbf{F}_1 = \mathbf{i} + 5\mathbf{j}$ acting at $A\ (3, -5)$, $\mathbf{F}_2 = 3\mathbf{i} - 2\mathbf{j}$ acting at $B\ (2, 6)$ and $\mathbf{F}_3 = 6\mathbf{i} + 21\mathbf{j}$ acting at $C\ (-2, 3)$.

4 Find the force, $\mathbf{F}$, and its line of action, which is equivalent to the forces $\mathbf{F}_1 = 8\mathbf{i} - 3\mathbf{j}$ acting at $A\ (-5, 4)$, $\mathbf{F}_2 = 6\mathbf{i} + 2\mathbf{j}$ acting at $B\ (3, 2)$ and $\mathbf{F}_3 = -2\mathbf{i} + 10\mathbf{j}$ acting at $C\ (4, 7)$.

5 Three forces, $\mathbf{F}_1$, $\mathbf{F}_2$ and $\mathbf{F}_3$, act on a rigid body at points A, B and C, respectively, where:

$\mathbf{F}_1 = 3\mathbf{i} - \mathbf{j} + 5\mathbf{k}$ acting at $A\ (4, 1, -2)$
$\mathbf{F}_2 = 2\mathbf{i} + 6\mathbf{j} - 12\mathbf{k}$ acting at $B\ (5, -2, 3)$
$\mathbf{F}_3 = -4\mathbf{i} + 3\mathbf{j} + 7\mathbf{k}$ acting at $C\ (1, -3, 6)$

(a) Find the single force, $\mathbf{F}$, acting at O and the couple, $\mathbf{G}$, which is equivalent to the three forces.

(b) Find the shortest distance from A to the line of action of $\mathbf{F}_2$.

6 Three forces, $\mathbf{F}_1$, $\mathbf{F}_2$ and $\mathbf{F}_3$, act on a rigid body at points A, B and C, respectively, where:

$\mathbf{F}_1 = \mathbf{i} - 3\mathbf{j} + 2\mathbf{k}$ acting at $A\ (-4, 2, -11)$
$\mathbf{F}_2 = 5\mathbf{i} + 4\mathbf{j} - \mathbf{k}$ acting at $B\ (5, 9, 7)$
$\mathbf{F}_3 = 3\mathbf{i} + 5\mathbf{j} - 7\mathbf{k}$ acting at $C\ (2, 4, 5)$

(a) Find the single force, $\mathbf{F}$, acting at O and the couple, $\mathbf{G}$, which is equivalent to the three forces.

(b) Find the shortest distance from B to the line of action of $\mathbf{F}_3$.

7 Three forces, $\mathbf{F}_1$, $\mathbf{F}_2$ and $\mathbf{F}_3$, act on a rigid body at points A, B and C, respectively, where:

$\mathbf{F}_1 = 6\mathbf{i} + 4\mathbf{j} - 3\mathbf{k}$ acting at $A\ (1, -3, 4)$
$\mathbf{F}_2 = 2\mathbf{i} - 3\mathbf{j} - 5\mathbf{k}$ acting at $B\ (7, 3, -6)$
$\mathbf{F}_3 = 5\mathbf{i} - 6\mathbf{j} + 7\mathbf{k}$ acting at $C\ (-2, 5, 2)$

(a) Find the single force, $\mathbf{F}$, acting at O and the couple, $\mathbf{G}$, which is equivalent to the three forces.

(b) Find the shortest distance from C to the line of action of $\mathbf{F}_2$.

8 Three forces, $\mathbf{F}_1$, $\mathbf{F}_2$ and $\mathbf{F}_3$, act on a rigid body at points A, B and C, respectively, where:

$\mathbf{F}_1 = 3\mathbf{i} - 4\mathbf{j} + 5\mathbf{k}$ acting at A (5, 2, −6)
$\mathbf{F}_2 = 7\mathbf{i} + 3\mathbf{j} - 6\mathbf{k}$ acting at B (5, 8, 7)
$\mathbf{F}_3 = -4\mathbf{i} + 6\mathbf{j} - 3\mathbf{k}$ acting at C (−2, 3, −8)

(a) Find the single force, $\mathbf{F}$, acting at O and the couple, $\mathbf{G}$, which is equivalent to the three forces.

(b) Find the shortest distance from A to the line of action of $\mathbf{F}_3$.

9 The square $ABCD$ has each side of length 6 m. Forces of magnitude 1, 2, 8, 5, $5\sqrt{2}$ and $2\sqrt{2}$ N, respectively, act along AB, BC, CD, DA, AC and DB, respectively, in the directions indicated by the order of the letters. Prove that these forces are equivalent to a couple. Calculate the magnitude and direction of this couple. [A]

10 At time t s two forces, $\mathbf{F}_1$ and $\mathbf{F}_2$, are given by

$$\mathbf{F}_1 = (\mathbf{i}\cos t + \mathbf{j}\cos t + 2\mathbf{k}\sin t)\text{ N}$$
$$\mathbf{F}_2 = (\mathbf{i}\sin t + \mathbf{j}\sin t - \mathbf{k}\cos t)\text{ N}$$

The force $\mathbf{F}_1$ acts through the fixed origin O and the force $\mathbf{F}_2$ acts through the point with position vector $(\mathbf{i} + \mathbf{j} + \mathbf{k})$ m relative to O. Find the sum of the moments of the forces about the point with position vector $(a\mathbf{i} + b\mathbf{j} + c\mathbf{k})$ m, where a, b, c are constants, showing that the component of this sum in the direction of $\mathbf{i}$ is

$$((b + c - 1)\cos t + (c - 2b - 1)\sin t)\text{ N m}.$$

Hence, or otherwise, find the position vector of the point A (independent of time) such that the system of the two forces $\mathbf{F}_1$ and $\mathbf{F}_2$ reduces, for all values of t, to a single force at A. [A]

11 Forces $\mathbf{F}_1$ and $\mathbf{F}_2$, where

$$\mathbf{F}_1 = (4\mathbf{i} + 5\mathbf{j} + 2\mathbf{k})\text{ N},\ \mathbf{F}_2 = (3\mathbf{i} + \mathbf{j} + 4\mathbf{k})\text{ N}$$

act through the points with position vectors, referred to an origin O, $(a\mathbf{i} + 7\mathbf{j} + 3\mathbf{k})$ m and $(4\mathbf{i} + 3\mathbf{j} + a\mathbf{k})$ m, respectively, where a is a constant. Given that the lines of action of the forces intersect at a point, find:

(a) the value of a,

(b) a vector equation of the line of action of the resultant of the forces $\mathbf{F}_1$ and $\mathbf{F}_2$,

(c) the sum of the moments of $\mathbf{F}_1$ and $\mathbf{F}_2$ about O. [A]

12 Two forces, $\mathbf{F}_1 = (\mathbf{i} + \mathbf{j} + 2\mathbf{k})$ N and $\mathbf{F}_2 = (2\mathbf{i} - \mathbf{j} + \mathbf{k})$ N, act at the points whose position vectors relative to an origin O are $\mathbf{r}_1 = (\mathbf{i} + 2\mathbf{k})$ m and $\mathbf{r}_2 = (2\mathbf{j} - \mathbf{k})$ m, respectively.

(a) Determine the shortest distance between the lines of action of these forces.

(b) Find the force, $\mathbf{R}$, at the origin and the couple, $\mathbf{G}$, to which the system reduces.

(c) Determine the moment, $\mathbf{G}'$, of the forces $\mathbf{F}_1$ and $\mathbf{F}_2$ about the point with position vector $x\mathbf{i} + y\mathbf{j} + z\mathbf{k}$. Hence, or otherwise, show that $\mathbf{R}.\mathbf{G}'$ is independent of x, y and z.

[A]

13 A triangle has vertices at the points O (0, 0), A (1, 0) and B (0, 1) referred to Cartesian axes Ox and Oy. Forces of magnitude 4 N, 2 N and $5\sqrt{2}$ N act along $\overrightarrow{OA}$, $\overrightarrow{OB}$ and $\overrightarrow{AB}$, respectively. Let $\mathbf{i}$ and $\mathbf{j}$ be unit vectors along Ox and Oy.

(a) Calculate the resultant of this system of forces, expressing it in the form $\alpha\mathbf{i} + \beta\mathbf{j}$, and find the point where the line of action of this resultant cuts the x-axis.

(b) An extra force, P, is added at A so that the magnitude of the resultant becomes zero. Explain why this force system is equivalent to a couple and find its moment.

[A]

14 The diagram shows the cube $ABCDEFGH$, which has sides of length 2.

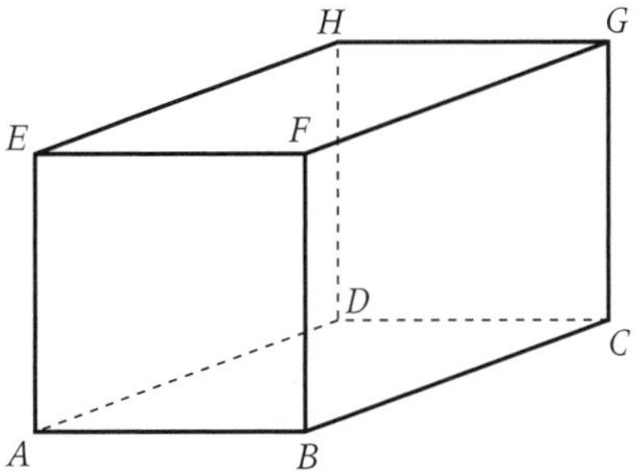

Forces act at the corners as listed below:

B	$4\mathbf{i} - 2\mathbf{j}$
C	$4\mathbf{i} + 2\mathbf{j}$
E	$-2\mathbf{j} + 4\mathbf{k}$
H	$2\mathbf{j} + \mathbf{k}$

The unit vector $\mathbf{i}$ is parallel to AB, the unit vector $\mathbf{j}$ is parallel to AD and the unit vector $\mathbf{k}$ is parallel to AE.

(a) Find the resultant force acting on the cube.

(b) Find the total moment about the corner A of the four forces acting on the cube.

(c) An additional force acts at a point on the edge AD, so that the cube is in equilibrium. Find this force and the coordinates of the point at which it acts. [A]

Key point summary

1 The scalar product of two vectors **a** and **b**, of magnitude a and b respectively, is defined as p 1

$$a\,b\cos\theta$$

where θ is the angle measured in an anticlockwise direction between **a** and **b**. The scalar product of the two vectors **a** and **b** is denoted by **a.b**.

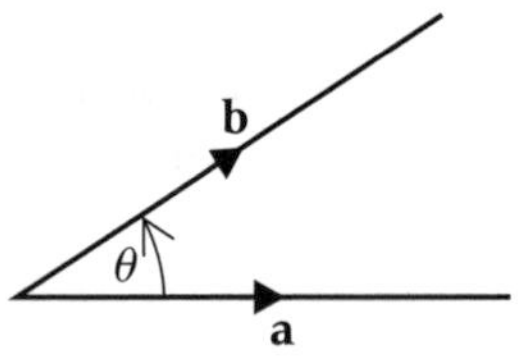

2 The scalar products of the unit vectors **i**, **j** and **k** can be found. First note that, p 2

$$\mathbf{i.i} = \mathbf{j.j} = \mathbf{k.k} = 1,$$

since these are the products of parallel unit vectors. Similarly $\mathbf{i.j} = 0$, since the angle between **i** and **j** is 90°. In the same way, $\mathbf{i.k} = \mathbf{j.k} = 0$.

3 $\mathbf{a.b} = ab\cos\theta = a_1b_1 + a_2b_2 + a_3b_3$ p 2

4 If a force, **F**, acts on a body as its displacement changes by **r**, then the work done is $Fr\cos\theta$, where F is the magnitude of the force and r is the magnitude of the displacement. p 5
That is,

$$\text{Work done} = \mathbf{F.r}$$

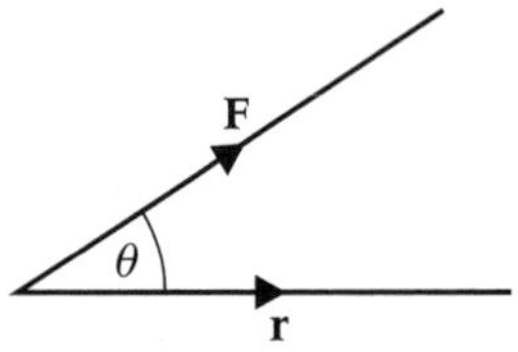

5 The **vector product** or **cross product** of vectors **a** and **b** is denoted by $\mathbf{a} \times \mathbf{b}$ or $\mathbf{a} \wedge \mathbf{b}$, p 8
and the **vector product** is defined as $ab\sin\theta\,\mathbf{n}$ where θ is the angle in the anticlockwise sense between **a** and **b**, and **n** is a unit vector, so that **a**, **b** and **n** form a right-handed set.

6 p 9

$$\mathbf{a} \times \mathbf{b} = \begin{vmatrix} \mathbf{i} & \mathbf{j} & \mathbf{k} \\ a_1 & a_2 & a_3 \\ b_1 & b_2 & b_3 \end{vmatrix}$$

7 The moment, **M**, of the force is given by p 12

$$\mathbf{M} = \mathbf{r} \times \mathbf{F}$$

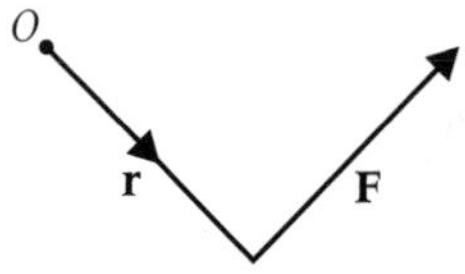

8 When you are using vector techniques, systems of coplanar forces are equivalent if and only if: p 14

(a) the vector sums of the two force systems are equal,

(b) the resulting moment about any point in the plane containing the forces is identical in both systems.

Both of these conditions need to be satisfied if the two force systems are to be equivalent.

9 A system of **coplanar** forces reduces to a couple if both of the following conditions are satisfied: p 20

(a) the resultant force is zero,

(b) the resultant moment about any point in the plane is non-zero.

An alternative condition is that the resultant moment about any three non-colinear points is non-zero.

10 Three or more forces can always be made equivalent to a force which passes through any chosen point together with a couple. p 24
A couple and a force cannot, in three dimensions, normally be combined into one force.

Test yourself	What to review
1 Find the angle between the two forces $\mathbf{F}_1 = (6\mathbf{i} + 8\mathbf{j} - 9\mathbf{k})$ N and $\mathbf{F}_2 = (8\mathbf{i} + 2\mathbf{j} + 7\mathbf{k})$ N.	*Section 1.1*
2 Calculate the work done when the force $(9\mathbf{i} + 8\mathbf{j} + 7\mathbf{k})$ N acts on a body as it is displaced from the point with coordinates (8, −4, −5) to the point with coordinates (7, −2, 9).	*Section 1.1*
3 Given that $\mathbf{a} = 4\mathbf{i} - 2\mathbf{j} + \mathbf{k}$ and $\mathbf{b} = \mathbf{i} + 6\mathbf{j} - 2\mathbf{k}$, find: **(a)** $\mathbf{a} \times \mathbf{b}$, **(b)** the sine of the angle between **a** and **b**.	*Section 1.2*
4 The force $4\mathbf{i} + 6\mathbf{j} - 9\mathbf{k}$ acts at the point (4, 7, −2). **(a)** Find the moment of this force about the origin. **(b)** Find the moment of this force about the point (4, 2, 1).	*Section 1.3*
5 Find the force, **F**, and its line of action, which is equivalent to the forces $\mathbf{F}_1 = 5\mathbf{i} - 8\mathbf{j}$ acting at (2, 3) and $\mathbf{F}_2 = 2\mathbf{i} + 3\mathbf{j}$ acting at (2, −4).	*Section 1.4*
6 Three forces act on a body. $\mathbf{F}_1 = 6\mathbf{i} - 2\mathbf{j} + 8\mathbf{k}$, which acts at (0, 2, 3) $\mathbf{F}_2 = 5\mathbf{i} - \mathbf{j}$, which acts at (5, 0, 7) $\mathbf{F}_3 = 4\mathbf{i} - 2\mathbf{j} + 3\mathbf{k}$, which acts at (5, 2, 4). These forces are equivalent to a single force, **F**, and a couple, **G**, applied at the origin. Find **F** and **G**.	*Section 1.4*

Test yourself ANSWERS

1 89.6°.

2 105 J.

3 **(a)** $-2\mathbf{i} + 9\mathbf{j} + 26\mathbf{k}$; **(b)** $\sqrt{\frac{761}{861}}$.

4 **(a)** $-51\mathbf{i} + 28\mathbf{j} - 4\mathbf{k}$; **(b)** $-27\mathbf{i} - 12\mathbf{j} - 20\mathbf{k}$.

5 $\mathbf{F} = 7\mathbf{i} - 5\mathbf{j}$, $\mathbf{r} = \begin{pmatrix} 3.4 \\ 0 \end{pmatrix} + \lambda \begin{pmatrix} 7 \\ -5 \end{pmatrix}$.

6 $\mathbf{F} = 15\mathbf{i} - 5\mathbf{j} + 11\mathbf{k}$, $\mathbf{G} = 43\mathbf{i} + 54\mathbf{j} - 35\mathbf{k}$.

The motion of a projectile on an inclined plane

Learning objectives

After studying this chapter you should be able to:

- use the components of acceleration parallel and perpendicular to the plane to solve problems
- calculate the time of flight and range of a projectile on an inclined plane.

2.1 The path of a projectile on an inclined plane

You will recall the results for projectile motion from the M1 module. The acceleration is given by

$$\mathbf{a} = -g\mathbf{j}.$$

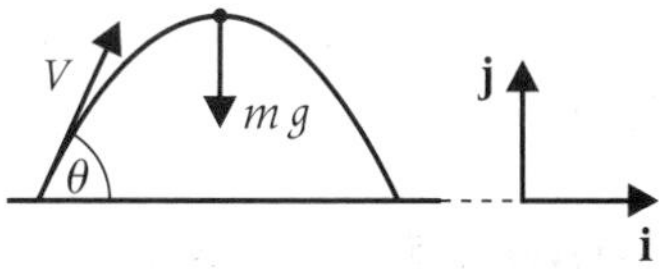

The velocity is given by

$$\mathbf{v} = V\cos\theta\,\mathbf{i} + (V\sin\theta - gt)\mathbf{j}.$$

The position vector is

$$\mathbf{r} = V\cos\theta t\,\mathbf{i} + \left(V\sin\theta t - \tfrac{1}{2}gt^2\right)\mathbf{j}.$$

These results were all derived by finding the acceleration of the projectile and then using the constant acceleration equations.

When a projectile moves on an inclined plane rather than on a horizontal plane, the best approach is to use unit vectors which are parallel and perpendicular to the plane. The diagram shows an inclined plane, the path of the projectile and the unit vectors **i** and **j**.

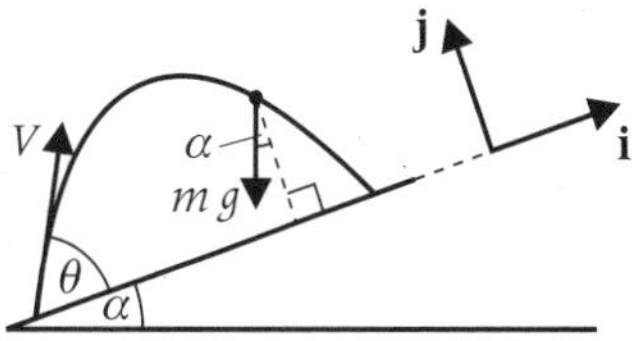

We make the same key assumption that the weight of the projectile is the only force that acts on it as it moves. The resultant force, **F**, on a projectile of mass m is then

$$\mathbf{F} = -mg\sin\alpha\,\mathbf{i} - mg\cos\alpha\,\mathbf{j}.$$

> The acceleration, **a**, of a projectile on an inclined plane will be
>
> $$\mathbf{a} = -g\sin\alpha\,\mathbf{i} - g\cos\alpha\,\mathbf{j}$$

The initial velocity, **u**, will be given by

$$\mathbf{u} = V\cos\theta\,\mathbf{i} + V\sin\theta\,\mathbf{j}.$$

The velocity of the projectile can now be found using the constant acceleration equation

$$\begin{aligned}\mathbf{v} &= \mathbf{u} + \mathbf{a}t \\ &= V\cos\theta\,\mathbf{i} + V\sin\theta\,\mathbf{j} + (-g\sin\alpha\,\mathbf{i} - g\cos\alpha\,\mathbf{j})t \\ &= (V\cos\theta - g\sin\alpha t)\,\mathbf{i} + (V\sin\theta - g\cos\alpha t)\,\mathbf{j}\end{aligned}$$

The position vector can also be found, assuming that the projectile begins to move from the origin.

$$\begin{aligned}\mathbf{r} &= \mathbf{u}t + \tfrac{1}{2}\mathbf{a}t^2 \\ &= (V\cos\theta\,\mathbf{i} + V\sin\theta\,\mathbf{j})t + \tfrac{1}{2}(-g\sin\alpha\,\mathbf{i} - g\cos\alpha\,\mathbf{j})t^2 \\ &= \left(V\cos\theta t - \frac{g\sin\alpha t^2}{2}\right)\mathbf{i} + \left(V\sin\theta t - \frac{g\cos\alpha t^2}{2}\right)\mathbf{j}\end{aligned}$$

The result for the position of a projectile on an inclined plane can be used to solve many problems.

$$\mathbf{r} = \left(V\cos\theta t - \frac{g\sin\alpha t^2}{2}\right)\mathbf{i} + \left(V\sin\theta t - \frac{g\cos\alpha t^2}{2}\right)\mathbf{j}$$

The following examples illustrate how these results can be applied.

Worked example 2.1

A particle is projected from a plane inclined at an angle of 30° to the horizontal. The particle has an initial velocity of $20\,\mathrm{m\,s^{-1}}$ at an angle of 45° above the plane, so that it moves up the plane. Find the range of the particle. (Take $g = 10\,\mathrm{m\,s^{-2}}$.)

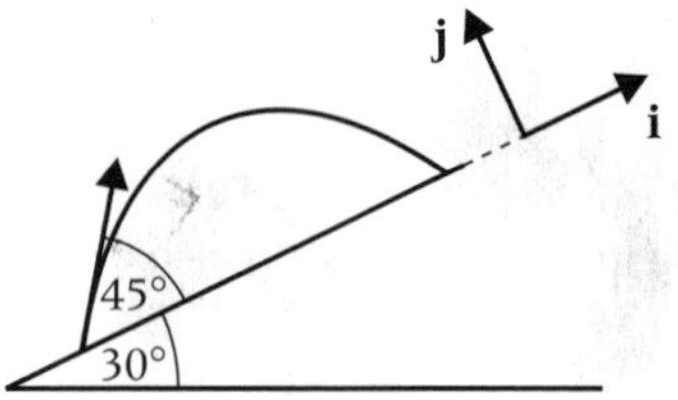

Solution

Taking the point where the particle is launched as the origin and using unit vectors **i** and **j** that are parallel and perpendicular to the plane gives the position vector, **r**, of the particle at time t as,

$$\begin{aligned}\mathbf{r} &= (20\cos 45^\circ t - 5\sin 30^\circ t^2)\,\mathbf{i} + (20\sin 45^\circ t - 5\cos 30^\circ t^2)\,\mathbf{j} \\ &= \left(\frac{20t}{\sqrt{2}} - \frac{5t^2}{2}\right)\mathbf{i} + \left(\frac{20t}{\sqrt{2}} - \frac{5\sqrt{3}t^2}{2}\right)\mathbf{j}\end{aligned}$$

When the particle hits the plane the component of the position vector perpendicular to the plane will be zero.

$$\frac{20t}{\sqrt{2}} - \frac{5\sqrt{3}t^2}{2} = 0$$

$$t = 0 \text{ or } t = 4\sqrt{\frac{2}{3}}$$

So the time of flight is $4\sqrt{\frac{2}{3}}$ s. This can now be substituted into the horizontal component of the position vector to give the range.

$$\begin{aligned}\text{Range} &= \frac{20}{\sqrt{2}} \times 4\sqrt{\frac{2}{3}} - \frac{5}{2} \times \left(4\sqrt{\frac{2}{3}}\right)^2 \\ &= \frac{80}{\sqrt{3}} - \frac{80}{3} \\ &= \frac{80(\sqrt{3}-1)}{3} \\ &= 19.5\,\text{m (to 3 sf)}\end{aligned}$$

Worked example 2.2

A projectile is launched with speed V, at an angle θ above a plane, which is inclined at an angle α above the horizontal. For this projectile find:

(a) the time of flight,
(b) the range on the plane,
(c) the maximum distance of the projectile from the plane.

Solution

(a) The time of flight will be found by considering when the component of the position vector perpendicular to the plane is zero. Using the result for the position vector derived above gives

$$V\sin\theta\, t - \frac{g\cos\alpha\, t^2}{2} = 0$$

$$\left(V\sin\theta - \frac{g\cos\alpha\, t}{2}\right)t = 0$$

$$t = 0 \text{ or } t = \frac{2V\sin\theta}{g\cos\alpha}$$

Hence the time of flight is

$$\frac{2V\sin\theta}{g\cos\alpha}.$$

(b) To find the range of the projectile substitute the time of flight into the expression for the component of the displacement parallel to the plane. This gives

$$\begin{aligned}\text{Range} &= V\cos\theta \times \frac{2V\sin\theta}{g\cos\alpha} - \frac{g\sin\alpha}{2} \times \left(\frac{2V\sin\theta}{g\cos\alpha}\right)^2 \\ &= \frac{2V^2\sin\theta}{g\cos^2\alpha}(\cos\theta\cos\alpha - \sin\theta\sin\alpha) \\ &= \frac{2V^2\sin\theta\cos(\alpha+\theta)}{g\cos^2\alpha}\end{aligned}$$

(c) The projectile will be at its maximum distance from the plane when the component of the velocity perpendicular to the plane is zero.

$$V \sin\theta - g\cos\alpha t = 0$$

$$t = \frac{V\sin\theta}{g\cos\alpha}$$

Substituting this value of t into the component of the displacement perpendicular to the plane gives

$$\text{Maximum height} = V\sin\theta \times \frac{V\sin\theta}{g\cos\alpha} - \frac{g\cos\alpha}{2} \times \left(\frac{V\sin\theta}{g\cos\alpha}\right)^2$$

$$= \frac{V^2\sin^2\theta}{2g\cos\alpha}$$

Worked example 2.3

A projectile is launched with speed V, at an angle θ above a plane, which is inclined at an angle α above the horizontal.

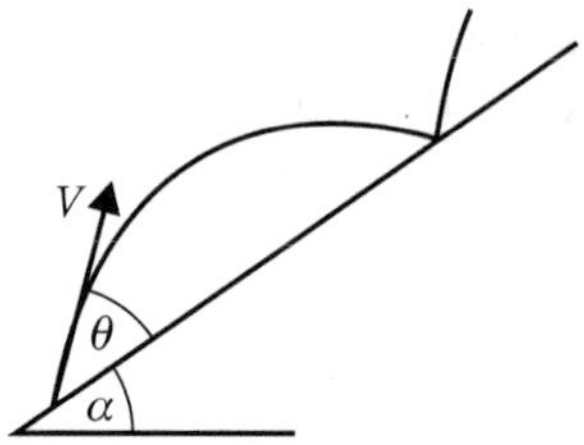

(a) Show that it follows the path illustrated in the diagram, where it bounces up the plane provided

$$\tan\alpha < \frac{1}{2\tan\theta}.$$

(b) Describe what happens if

$$\tan\alpha = \frac{1}{2\tan\theta}.$$

Solution

(a) For the projectile to bounce up the plane the component of the velocity parallel to the plane must be greater than zero when the projectile hits the plane.

The component of the velocity of the projectile parallel to the plane is $V\cos\theta - g\sin\alpha t$ and when the projectile hits the plane for the first time

$$t = \frac{2V\sin\theta}{g\cos\alpha}.$$

As the component parallel to the plane is greater than zero,

$$V\cos\theta - g\sin\alpha t > 0$$

and then substituting for t, the time when the projectile hits the plane, gives

$$V\cos\theta - g\sin\alpha \times \frac{2V\sin\theta}{g\cos\alpha} > 0$$

$$\frac{1}{2\tan\theta} - \tan\alpha > 0$$

$$\tan\alpha < \frac{1}{2\tan\theta}$$

(b) If $\tan\alpha = \dfrac{1}{2\tan\theta}$, the component of the velocity perpendicular to the plane will be zero, when the projectile hits the plane. This means that the projectile will initially rebound at right angles to the plane. Due to the fact that the projectile has a component of its acceleration down the plane the projectile will accelerate in this direction and move down the plane.

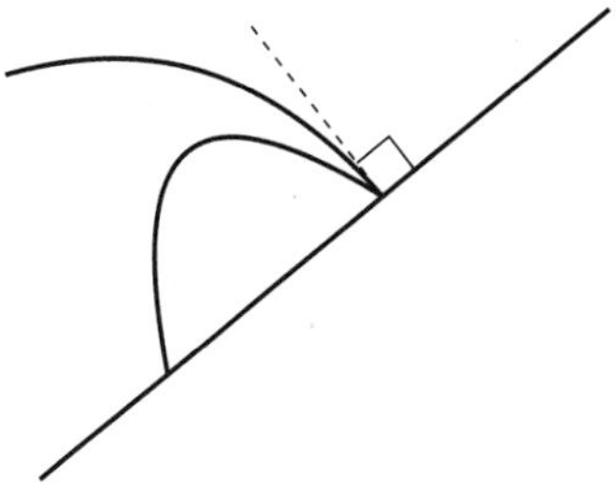

EXERCISE 2A

In all these questions assume that the motion takes place in a vertical plane that contains the line of greatest slope of the plane.

1 A projectile is launched on a plane that is inclined at an angle of 10° to the horizontal. The ball has an initial speed of $12\,\text{m}\,\text{s}^{-1}$ at an angle of 30° above the plane, as shown in the diagram.

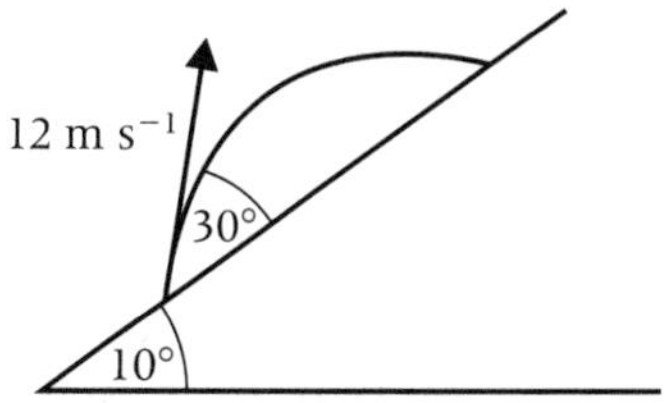

(a) Find the time of flight of the projectile.

(b) Find the range of the projectile.

(c) Find the maximum distance between the projectile and the plane.

2 A ball is kicked on a pitch that is inclined at an angle of 3° above the horizontal. The ball has an initial velocity of $15\,\text{m}\,\text{s}^{-1}$ at an angle of 40° to the plane. The ball moves up the slope.

(a) Assume that the pitch is horizontal and calculate the range of the ball.

(b) Calculate the range of the ball on the sloping pitch and compare your two ranges.

3 A car is travelling on a horizontal surface at a speed of $30\,\text{m}\,\text{s}^{-1}$, when it reaches a ramp as shown in the diagram. Find the distance between the top of the ramp and the point where the car hits the ramp.

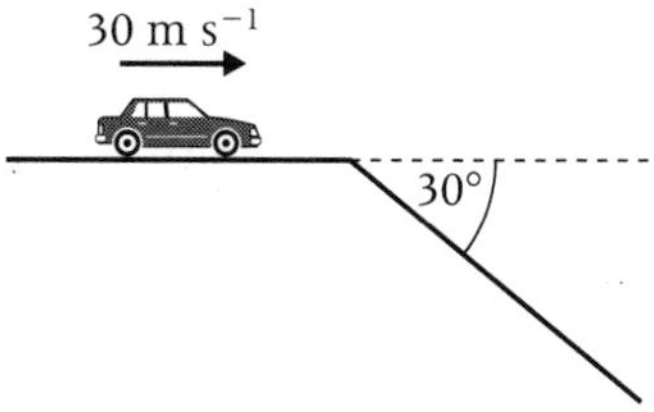

4 A tank is set so that it fires shells at a speed $120\,\text{m}\,\text{s}^{-1}$ at an angle of 45° above the plane on which it is resting. Calculate the percentage reduction in the range of the shell, when it is fired up a plane angled at 20° to the horizontal, compared to a horizontal surface.

5 A golfer practises hitting a ball on a slope that is inclined at an angle of 8° to the horizontal. He hits the ball, so that it initially moves at $40\,\text{m}\,\text{s}^{-1}$ and at an angle of 40° to the slope. Find the two possible ranges for the ball.

6 A projectile is launched on a plane inclined at an angle α above the horizontal, as shown in the diagram. The projectile initially moves at an angle θ above the plane and with speed V. Find an expression for the range of the projectile on this plane.

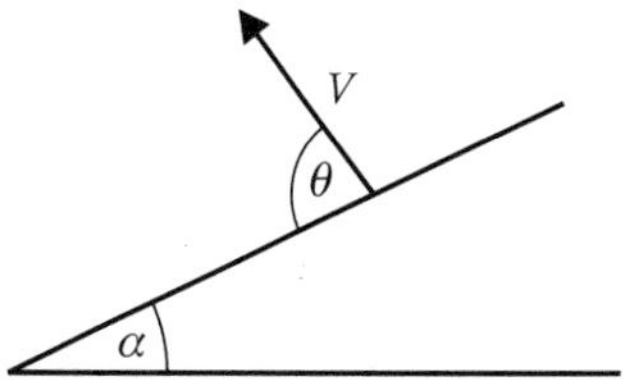

7 A projectile is launched with speed V, at an angle θ above a plane, which is inclined at an angle α above the horizontal. The projectile is initially on the plane. Show that the magnitude of the component of the velocity perpendicular to the plane when the projectile is launched is the same as when it hits the plane.

8 **(a)** Prove that

$$2 \sin\theta \cos(\alpha + \theta) = \sin(2\theta + \alpha) - \sin\alpha.$$

A projectile is launched on a plane inclined at an angle α above the horizontal. The projectile initially moves at an angle θ above the plane and with speed V.

(b) Show that the maximum range of the projectile is

$$\frac{V^2(1 - \sin\alpha)}{g\cos^2\alpha}.$$

(c) Find the value of θ , in terms of α, for which the maximum range will be achieved.

9 A projectile is launched on a plane inclined at an angle α above the horizontal. The projectile initially moves at an angle θ above the horizontal and with speed V.

Find the range of the projectile in terms of V, α, θ and g.

10 A sprinkler sprays water at an angle of 30° above the plane on which it is resting. The sprinkler is placed on a slope inclined at 10° to the horizontal. The water reaches a point 5 m up the slope from the sprinkler. Find the speed at which the water leaves the sprinkler.

11 A bank is inclined at 20° to the horizontal. A child kicks a ball from a point on the bank at an angle θ above the slope of the bank. The ball is initially kicked with a speed of $8\,\text{m}\,\text{s}^{-1}$. Find the range of values of θ for which the ball continues to move up the slope after it has bounced for the first time.

12 A stunt motorcyclist drives up the ramp, AB, shown in the diagram. At B the motorcycle leaves the ramp and moves under gravity until it hits the slope BC at the point P.

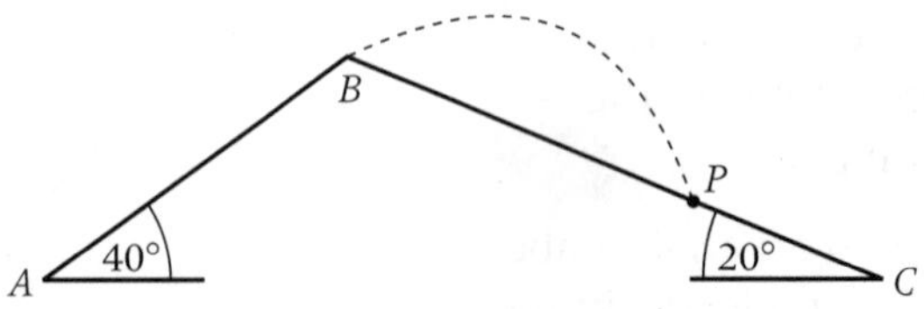

At what speed should the motorcyclist drive up the first ramp to make the distance between B and P be 12 m?

13 A particle is projected with speed U from a point O, which is on a plane inclined at an angle of 30° to the horizontal. The angle of projection of the particle is at 60° above the horizontal. The particle hits the plane at the point B, that is up the slope and a distance R from O.

(a) Show that the time of flight of the particle, as it travels from O to B, is $\dfrac{2U}{g\sqrt{3}}$.

(b) Find R. [A]

Key point summary

1 The acceleration, **a**, of a projectile on an inclined plane will be *p 33*

$$\mathbf{a} = -g \sin \alpha \, \mathbf{i} - g \cos \alpha \, \mathbf{j}$$

2 The result for the position of a projectile on an inclined plane can be used to solve many problems. *p 34*

$$\mathbf{r} = \left(V \cos \theta t - \frac{g \sin \alpha t^2}{2} \right) \mathbf{i} + \left(V \sin \theta t - \frac{g \cos \alpha t^2}{2} \right) \mathbf{j}$$

Test yourself

What to review

1 A golfer hits a ball that is on a plane inclined at 8° to the horizontal. The ball moves in a vertical plane that contains the line of greatest slope of the plane. The ball initially moves at $20\,\mathrm{m\,s^{-1}}$ and at an angle of 60° above the plane. Determine the time to the first bounce of the ball and the distance from its initial position. *Section 2.1*

Test yourself ANSWERS

1 3.57 s, 27.0 m.

CHAPTER 3

Forced and damped harmonic motion

Learning objectives

After studying this chapter you should be able to:

- set up and solve differential equations to model damped motion
- know and be able to identify the three different types of damping: light, critical and heavy
- set up and solve differential equations to model forced motion
- be aware of when resonance will take place.

3.1 Damped harmonic motion

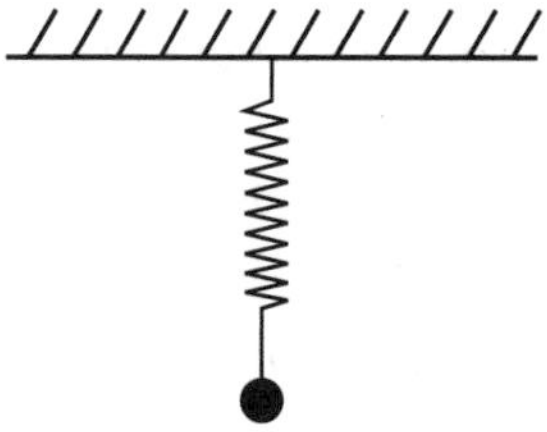

One end of an elastic string is attached to a fixed point. A particle is then hung from the string. The particle will rest in equilibrium. We found in M2 that if the particle is pulled down from the equilibrium position and released it will oscillate with simple harmonic motion about the equilibrium position. Using the assumptions in M2 the particle will continue to oscillate with the same amplitude indefinitely. In reality, the amplitude of its oscillation will decrease until it comes to rest.

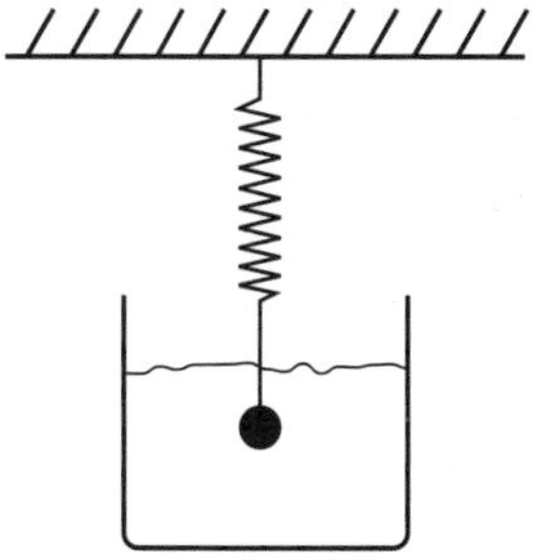

If the particle hangs in a bucket of water, you will find that it comes to rest much more rapidly. The slowing down of the particle is caused by air resistance or resistance to motion in a liquid. Mathematically, the damped motion is caused by a damping force, which, in this module, you may take to be proportional to the particle's velocity. The application of this force results in the particle moving with damped harmonic motion.

> We will often use the abbreviations $\dot{x} = \dfrac{dx}{dt}$ and $\ddot{x} = \dfrac{d^2x}{dt^2}$ in the following examples.

Worked example 3.1

A particle, of mass m, is attached to the end of a spring with modulus of elasticity λ. Initially the particle hangs in equilibrium. It is then pulled down below the equilibrium position and released from rest below the equilibrium position. As it moves, with speed v, the particle experiences an air resistance force of magnitude mkv, where k is a constant. Find the equation of motion for the particle.

Solution

The particle will oscillate in the vertical plane. The central point of its oscillations will be the equilibrium position. We will consider the particle's displacement from this central point. Take x to be the displacement of the particle, at time t, **below** the equilibrium position.

Note that since x is measured downwards from the equilibrium position, $\dot{x}$ and $\ddot{x}$ are also both positive when directed downwards.

When the particle is released from rest it will move upwards. However you need to know its equation of motion at a variable displacement x below its equilibrium position, so disregard the fact that the particle will move upwards when released.

Consider the particle at time t to be moving downwards with velocity $\dot{x}$.
The forces acting upon the particle are:

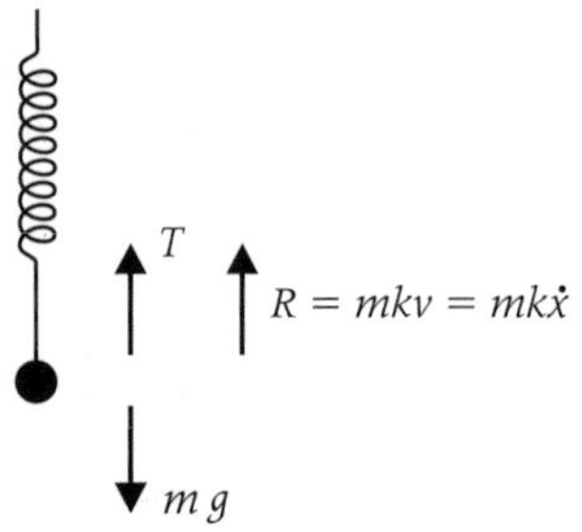

- gravity, vertically downwards,
- tension, vertically upwards,
- air resistance, R, which opposes motion.

When x is increasing, i.e., when the particle is moving downwards, the air resistance will be acting to oppose motion, hence it is acting vertically upwards. The air resistance mkv or $mk\dot{x}$ is acting **vertically upwards**.

Using $F = ma = m\ddot{x}$ vertically downwards gives

$$m\ddot{x} = mg - T - R$$
$$= mg - T - mk\dot{x}$$

or

$$m\frac{d^2x}{dt^2} + mk\frac{dx}{dt} + (T - mg) = 0. \qquad [1]$$

Since the extension in the string is $x + e$, where e is the extension in the equilibrium position,

$$T = \frac{\lambda(x+e)}{l}.$$

Also $\quad T_{\text{equilibrium}} = mg = \dfrac{\lambda e}{l}$

so $\quad e = \dfrac{lmg}{\lambda} \quad$ and $\quad T = \dfrac{\lambda x}{l} + \dfrac{\lambda e}{l} = \dfrac{\lambda x}{l} + mg.$

Hence equation [1] becomes

$$m\frac{d^2x}{dt^2} + mk\frac{dx}{dt} + \frac{\lambda x}{l} = 0$$

or

$$\frac{d^2x}{dt^2} + k\frac{dx}{dt} + \omega^2 x = 0$$

where $\omega^2 = \dfrac{\lambda}{ml}$ which is the value of ω^2 used for the motion of a simple mass–spring system.

This is the **governing differential equation** for the motion of the particle. You will note that if there is no air resistance acting, then $k = 0$ and you will obtain the usual simple harmonic motion equation.

Second order differential equations

Equations such as $\dfrac{d^2x}{dt^2} + k\dfrac{dx}{dt} + \omega^2 x = 0$ are linear second order differential equations.

We have already met equations such as $\dfrac{d^2x}{dt^2} + \omega^2 x = 0$, which was the equation for a particle moving subject to simple harmonic motion.

We now have to consider the solution of a more general linear second order differential equation such as that above.

The solution of a linear second order differential equation of the form

$$\frac{d^2x}{dt^2} + k\frac{dx}{dt} + \omega^2 x = 0$$

can be found by substituting $x = Ae^{mt}$, where m is a constant. Differentiating this expression for x gives

$$\frac{dx}{dt} = me^{mt} \quad \text{and} \quad \frac{d^2x}{dt^2} = m^2 e^{mt}.$$

Substituting into the differential equation now gives

$$m^2 e^{mt} + kme^{mt} + \omega^2 e^{mt} = 0$$
$$(m^2 + km + \omega^2)e^{mt} = 0$$

Since $e^{mt} \neq 0$ the values of m are given by the solutions of the quadratic equation

$$m^2 + km + \omega^2 = 0.$$

These solutions are given by

$$m = \frac{-k \pm \sqrt{k^2 - 4\omega^2}}{2}.$$

The solutions of the differential equation $\dfrac{d^2x}{dt^2} + k\dfrac{dx}{dt} + \omega^2 x = 0$, which models damped motion, are of the form $x = Ae^{mt}$, where $m = \dfrac{-k \pm \sqrt{k^2 - 4\omega^2}}{2}$. The number, and type of solutions of this quadratic equation depend on the value of $k^2 - 4\omega^2$.

There are three possible cases:

1 $k^2 - 4\omega^2 > 0$, the equation has two distinct roots,

2 $k^2 - 4\omega^2 = 0$, the equation has one (repeated) real root,

3 $k^2 - 4\omega^2 < 0$, the equation has two complex roots.

Each case will be considered separately.

Case 1: $k^2 - 4\omega^2 > 0$

In this case the roots of $m^2 + km + \omega^2 = 0$ will be of the form

$m = \dfrac{-k \pm \sqrt{k^2 - 4\omega^2}}{2}$, giving the two roots m_1 and m_2.

$$m_1 = -\frac{k}{2} + \frac{\sqrt{k^2 - 4\omega^2}}{2}$$

and

$$m_2 = -\frac{k}{2} - \frac{\sqrt{k^2 - 4\omega^2}}{2}.$$

Note that $m_2 < 0$.

So if $k^2 - 4\omega^2 > 0$, then the general solution of the differential equation is of the form

$$x = Ae^{m_1 t} + Be^{m_2 t}$$

where A and B are arbitrary constants.

To justify that this is a solution and in fact the full solution, we need to confirm

- there are two arbitrary constants as it was a **second** order differential equation, and
- that the solution does satisfy the equation

$$\frac{d^2x}{dt^2} + k\frac{dx}{dt} + \omega^2 x = 0.$$

You will notice that there are indeed the two required arbitrary constants.

To prove that the solution satisfies the equation, substitute the solution $x = Ae^{m_1 t} + Be^{m_2 t}$, into the left-hand side of

$$\frac{d^2x}{dt^2} + k\frac{dx}{dt} + \omega^2 x = 0$$

$$\begin{aligned}\frac{d^2x}{dt^2} + k\frac{dx}{dt} + \omega^2 x &= (m_1^2 Ae^{m_1 t} + m_2^2 Be^{m_2 t}) + k(m_1 Ae^{m_1 t} + m_2 Be^{m_2 t}) \\ &\quad + \omega^2(Ae^{m_1 t} + Be^{m_2 t}) \\ &= Ae^{m_1 t}(m_1^2 + km_1 + \omega^2) + Be^{m_2 t}(m_2^2 + km_2 + \omega^2) = 0\end{aligned}$$

since $m_1$and m_2 are roots of the equation $m^2 + km + \omega^2 = 0$.

To find the values of A and B you need two boundary or initial conditions.

If the motion begins from rest with a displacement a from the equilibrium position, then the initial condition below can be used.

$$x = a \text{ and } \dot{x} = 0, \text{ when } t = 0.$$

This gives

$$a = A + B$$

and, since

$$\frac{dx}{dt} = Am_1 e^{m_1 t} + Bm_2 e^{m_2 t}$$

$\dot{x} = 0$ gives

$$0 = Am_1 + Bm_2$$

Solving, $a = A + \left(-A\dfrac{m_1}{m_2}\right)$

$$\Rightarrow \quad A = \frac{am_2}{(m_2 - m_1)}$$

and $\quad B = \dfrac{am_1}{(m_1 - m_2)}$

The solution of the differential equation is

$$x = \frac{am_2}{m_2 - m_1} e^{m_1 t} + \frac{am_1}{m_1 - m_2} e^{m_2 t}.$$

Returning to the values of m found from

$$\frac{d^2x}{dt^2} + k\frac{dx}{dt} + \omega^2 x = 0$$

which were

$$m_1 = -\frac{k}{2} + \frac{1}{2}\sqrt{k^2 - 4\omega^2} \text{ and}$$

$$m_2 = -\frac{k}{2} - \frac{1}{2}\sqrt{k^2 - 4\omega^2}$$

we have seen that $m_2 < 0$, and since $|\sqrt{k^2 - 4\omega^2}| < |k|$, m_1 is also negative.
Thus the general solution is of the form

$$x = Ae^{m_1 t} + Be^{m_2 t}$$

where both m_1 and m_2 are negative.
The fact that both m_1 and m_2 are negative is true for all motion of a particle subject to a damping force where $k^2 - 4\omega^2 > 0$.
As t increases, both $e^{m_1 t}$ and $e^{m_2 t}$ tend to zero, and hence

$$x \to 0 \text{ as } t \to \infty.$$

Worked example 3.2

Solve the differential equation

$$\frac{d^2x}{dt^2}+3\frac{dx}{dt}+\frac{5}{4}x=0.$$

Solution

Substituting $x = e^{mt}$ gives

$$m^2+3m+\frac{5}{4}=0$$

$$\Rightarrow \quad m=\frac{-3\pm\sqrt{9-5}}{2}$$

$$=\frac{-3\pm 2}{2}$$

$$=-\frac{1}{2} \text{ or } -\frac{5}{2}$$

Hence, the general solution is given by

$$x=Ae^{-\frac{1}{2}t}+Be^{-\frac{5}{2}t}.$$

Since both the terms in x are **negative exponential**, it is clear that x tends to zero as t increases. A graph of a typical solution is illustrated opposite.

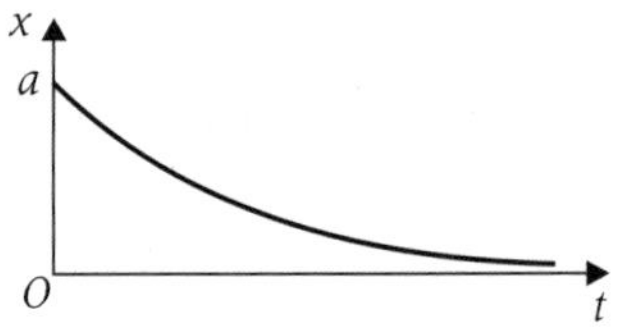

This is the case of **heavy damping** (or overdamping) in which the magnitude of the damping effect, modelled by the constant k, is so large that there is absolutely no oscillating motion at all.

The actual graph of x against t will depend on the initial conditions, i.e., the values of x and $\dot{x}$ and when $t = 0$.

The other possibilities for the graph of x against t are

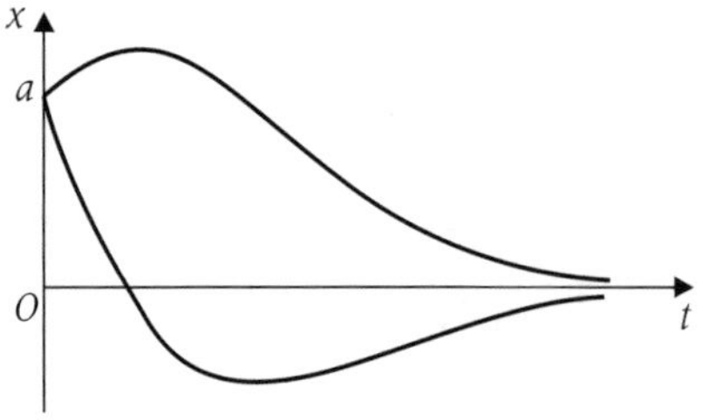

Case 2: $k^2 - 4\omega^2 = 0$

This time, the roots of

$$m^2+mk+\omega^2=0$$

are both real and equal to $-\frac{k}{2}$.

The solution is

$$x=(A+Bt)e^{-\frac{k}{2}t}.$$

You cannot just use $x = Ae^{-\frac{k}{2}t} + Be^{-\frac{k}{2}t}$ as above, since this simplifies to

$$x = (A + B)e^{-\frac{k}{2}t} = Ce^{-\frac{k}{2}t}$$

which has only **one** arbitrary constant and for a second order differential equation you need two arbitrary constants in the general solution.

To prove $x = (A + Bt)e^{-\frac{k}{2}t}$ is the solution, you must prove that it satisfies the equation

$$\frac{d^2x}{dt^2} + k\frac{dx}{dt} + \omega^2 x = 0.$$

Differentiating $x = (A + Bt)e^{-\frac{k}{2}t}$ gives,

$$\frac{dx}{dt} = Be^{-\frac{k}{2}t} - \frac{k}{2}e^{-\frac{k}{2}t}(A + Bt)$$

and

$$\frac{d^2x}{dt^2} = -\frac{k}{2}Be^{-\frac{k}{2}t} + \frac{k^2}{4}e^{-\frac{k}{2}t}(A + Bt) - \frac{k}{2}Be^{-\frac{k}{2}t}$$
$$= \frac{k^2}{4}e^{-\frac{k}{2}t}(A + Bt) - kBe^{-\frac{k}{2}t}$$

Substituting these into the left-hand side of the equation gives

$$\frac{d^2x}{dt^2} + k\frac{dx}{dt} + \omega^2 x$$
$$= \left[\frac{k^2}{4}e^{-\frac{k}{2}t}(A + Bt) - kBe^{-\frac{k}{2}t}\right] + k\left[Be^{-\frac{k}{2}t} - \frac{k}{2}e^{-\frac{k}{2}t}(A + Bt)\right]$$
$$+ \omega^2(A + Bt)e^{-\frac{k}{2}t}$$
$$= (A + Bt)e^{-\frac{k}{2}t}\left(\frac{k^2}{4} - \frac{k^2}{2} + \omega^2\right)$$

Since $k^2 - 4\omega^2 = 0$, this term is zero.

Hence $\frac{d^2x}{dt^2} + k\frac{dx}{dt} + \omega^2 x$ does equal 0.

So $x = (A + Bt)e^{-\frac{k}{2}t}$ is indeed the required solution.

As before to find the complete solution of

$$\frac{d^2x}{dt^2} + k\frac{dx}{dt} + \omega^2 x = 0$$

the initial conditions must be satisfied.

Using the same initial conditions as earlier the values of A and B can be determined.

At $t = 0$, $x = a$, so

$$a = A$$

Differentiating

$$\frac{dx}{dt} = -\frac{k}{2}e^{-\frac{k}{2}t}(A + Bt) + e^{-\frac{k}{2}t}B$$

At $t = 0$, $\dot{x} = 0$,

giving $\quad 0 = -\frac{k}{2}A + B$

Hence, $\quad B = \frac{ka}{2}$

and the complete solution is given by

$$x = ae^{-\frac{k}{2}t}\left(1 + \frac{k}{2}t\right)$$

or, in terms of ω,

$$x = ae^{-\omega t}(1 + \omega t)$$

Worked example 3.3

Find the general solution of the differential equation

$$\frac{d^2x}{dt^2} + \frac{dx}{dt} + \frac{1}{4}x = 0.$$

Solution

As before, substitute $x = e^{mt}$ in the differential equation, to give

$$m^2e^{mt} + me^{mt} + \frac{1}{4}e^{mt} = 0$$

$$\Rightarrow \quad \left(m^2 + m + \frac{1}{4}\right)e^{mt} = 0$$

$$\Rightarrow \quad m^2 + m + \frac{1}{4} = 0$$

$$\Rightarrow \quad \left(m + \frac{1}{2}\right)^2 = 0$$

Hence $m = -\frac{1}{2}$ (repeated), and the general solution is of the form

$$x = e^{-\frac{1}{2}t}(A + Bt).$$

This type of damping is referred to as **critical damping**, since it is the critical value of k which eradicates the oscillations you will find occur when $k^2 < 4\omega^2$.

A graph of a typical solution is shown.

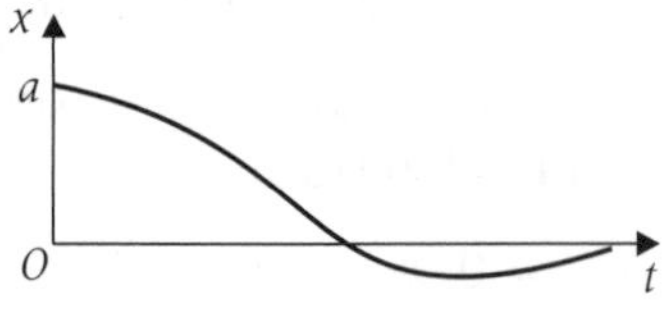

The actual graph of x against t will depend on the initial conditions, i.e., the values of x and $\dot{x}$ when $t = 0$.
You will notice that again x tends to zero as t tends to infinity.

Case 3: $k^2 - 4\omega^2 < 0$

Writing $\alpha^2 = 4\omega^2 - k^2$, the roots of the equation $m^2 + km + \omega^2 = 0$ can now be written as

$$m = \frac{-k \pm \sqrt{-\alpha^2}}{2}$$
$$= -\frac{k}{2} \pm i\frac{\alpha}{2}$$

So the roots are given by

$$m_1 = -\frac{k}{2} + i\frac{\alpha}{2} \quad \text{and} \quad m_2 = -\frac{k}{2} - i\frac{\alpha}{2}.$$

The general solution is now given by

$$x = Ae^{m_1 t} + Be^{m_2 t} \ (A \text{ and } B \text{ are arbitrary constants}).$$

This can be simplified, using the properties of indices and complex numbers:

$$x = Ae^{\left(-\frac{k}{2} + i\frac{\alpha}{2}\right)t} + Be^{\left(-\frac{k}{2} - i\frac{\alpha}{2}\right)t}$$
$$= Ae^{-\frac{k}{2}t}e^{i\frac{\alpha}{2}t} + Be^{-\frac{k}{2}t}e^{-i\frac{\alpha}{2}t}$$
$$= e^{-\frac{k}{2}t}\left(Ae^{i\frac{\alpha}{2}t} + Be^{-i\frac{\alpha}{2}t}\right)$$
$$= e^{-\frac{k}{2}t}\left[A\left(\cos\frac{\alpha}{2}t + i\sin\frac{\alpha}{2}t\right) + B\left(\cos\left(-\frac{\alpha}{2}t\right) + i\sin\left(-\frac{\alpha}{2}t\right)\right)\right]$$
$$= e^{-\frac{k}{2}t}\left[(A+B)\cos\frac{\alpha}{2}t + i(A-B)\sin\frac{\alpha}{2}t\right]$$

and writing new arbitrary constants

$$C = A + B$$
$$D = i(A - B)$$

gives the solution

$$x = e^{-\frac{k}{2}t}\left(C\cos\frac{\alpha}{2}t + D\sin\frac{\alpha}{2}t\right), \ \alpha = \sqrt{4\omega^2 - k^2}.$$

To complete the solution, the initial conditions must be applied.

At $t = 0$, $x = a$,

so $\quad a = C$

Also, $$\frac{dx}{dt} = -\frac{k}{2}e^{-\frac{k}{2}t}\left(C\cos\frac{\alpha}{2}t + D\sin\frac{\alpha}{2}t\right) + e^{-\frac{k}{2}t}\left(-C\frac{\alpha}{2}\sin\frac{\alpha}{2}t + D\frac{\alpha}{2}\cos\frac{\alpha}{2}t\right)$$

and, at $t = 0$, $\dot{x} = 0$ giving

$$0 = -\frac{k}{2}C + D\frac{\alpha}{2}.$$

Thus $\quad D = \dfrac{ka}{\alpha}$

and the complete solution is given by

$$x = ae^{-\frac{k}{2}t}\left(\cos\frac{\alpha}{2}t + \frac{k}{\alpha}\sin\frac{\alpha}{2}t\right).$$

Note that:

(a) the particle still oscillates but with reduced period

$$\frac{2\pi}{\left(\frac{\alpha}{2}\right)} = \frac{4\pi}{\sqrt{4\omega^2 - k^2}} = \frac{2\pi}{\sqrt{\omega^2 - \frac{1}{4}k^2}}$$

$\left(\text{note, again, that if } k = 0, \text{ the result returns to } \dfrac{2\pi}{\omega}\right)$,

(b) the amplitude, due to the $e^{-\frac{k}{2}t}$ term, decreases with time.

The graph opposite illustrates the motion.

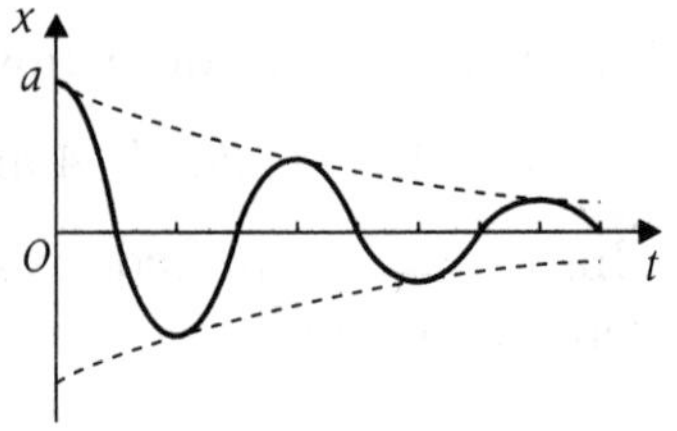

Worked example 3.4

Find the general solution of the differential equation governing damped harmonic motion when

$$\frac{d^2x}{dt^2} + \frac{1}{2}\frac{dx}{dt} + \frac{1}{4}x = 0.$$

Solution

Let $x = e^{mt}$

$$\Rightarrow \quad \frac{dx}{dt} = me^{mt}, \quad \frac{d^2x}{dt^2} = m^2e^{mt}$$

Substituting in the differential equation gives

$$m^2e^{mt} + \frac{1}{2}me^{mt} + \frac{1}{4}e^{mt} = 0$$

$$\left(m^2 + \frac{1}{2}m + \frac{1}{4}\right)e^{mt} = 0$$

This gives

$$m^2 + \frac{1}{2}m + \frac{1}{4} = 0$$

$$m = \frac{-\frac{1}{2} \pm \sqrt{\frac{1}{4} - 1}}{2}$$

$$= -\frac{1}{4} \pm \frac{1}{2}\sqrt{-\frac{3}{4}}$$

$$= -\frac{1}{4} \pm \frac{1}{4}\sqrt{3}i$$

So the roots are $m_1 = -\frac{1}{4} + \frac{1}{4}\sqrt{3}i$ and $m_2 = -\frac{1}{4} - \frac{1}{4}\sqrt{3}i$, and the solution is of the form

$$x = Ae^{\left(-\frac{1}{4}+\frac{1}{4}\sqrt{3}i\right)t} + Be^{\left(-\frac{1}{4}-\frac{1}{4}\sqrt{3}i\right)t}$$

$$\Rightarrow \quad x = e^{-\frac{1}{4}t}\left(C\cos\frac{\sqrt{3}}{4}t + D\sin\frac{\sqrt{3}}{4}t\right)$$

(using the same analysis as before).

This type of damping is sometimes referred to as **light damping**. Although the form of the solution is changed, the particle still oscillates, but with its amplitude reducing to zero.

3

Worked example 3.5

A particle, P, is attached to one end of a light elastic spring. The other end of the spring is attached to a fixed point O on a smooth horizontal table. The particle moves on the table along the line of the spring and, in addition to the force exerted by the spring, it is also acted on by a resistive force which is directly proportional to its speed. When the extension of the spring is 0.1 m and the particle is moving in the sense from O to P with speed 0.2 m s^{-1}, the total force on it in the direction $\vec{OP}$ is -0.09 N. When the spring is compressed by an amount of 0.1 m and the particle is moving in the sense from O to P with speed 0.25 m s^{-1}, the force acting on it is zero. Given that the mass of P is 0.1 kg, and given also that the spring has natural length 1.2 m, find its modulus of elasticity; hence show that the extension, x m of the spring at any time t s satisfies

$$\frac{d^2x}{dt^2} + 2\frac{dx}{dt} + 5x = 0.$$

When $t = 0$ the extension of the spring is 0.2 m and P is moving with speed 0.4 m s^{-1} in the sense from O to P. Find x for all values of t. [A]

Solution

In the first position, assuming the resistive force is of the form $R = k\dot{x}$

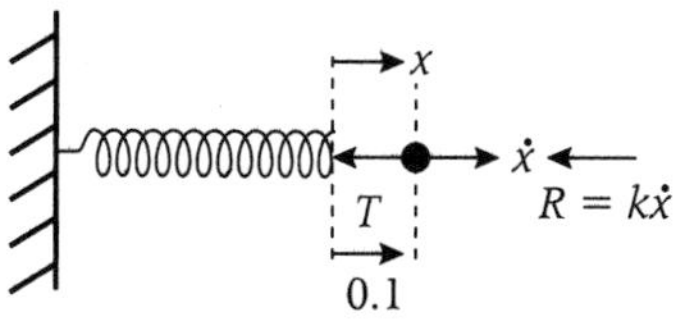

$$T + k\dot{x} = 0.09$$

and $\quad T = \frac{\lambda(0.1)}{l}, \; \dot{x} = 0.2$

giving $\quad (0.1)\frac{\lambda}{l} + k(0.2) = 0.09.$

In the second position, since the spring is in compression, and the particle is in equilibrium,

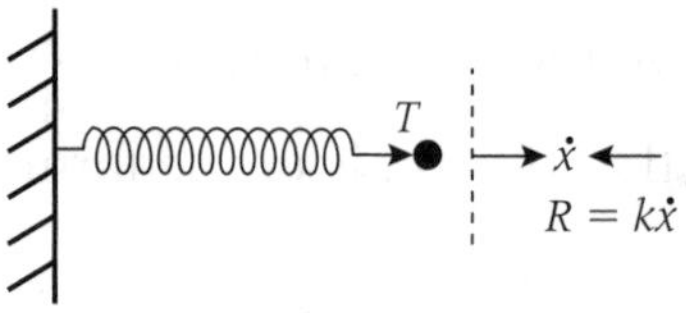

$$T = k\dot{x}$$

giving $\quad (0.1)\frac{\lambda}{l} = k(0.25).$

Using these two equations,

$$0.25k + 0.2k = 0.09 \Rightarrow k = 0.2$$

and, since $l = 1.2$,

$$\lambda = \frac{(0.2) \times (0.25) \times (1.2)}{(0.1)} = 0.6.$$

The differential equation for motion is

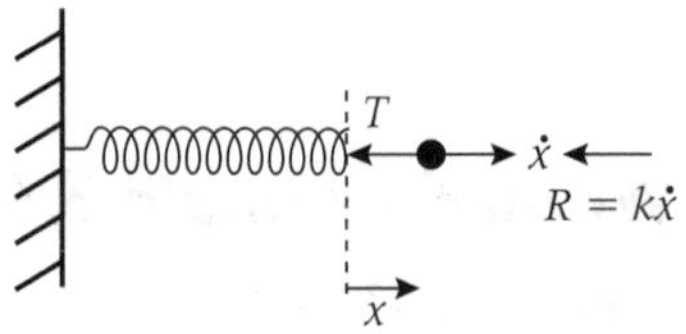

$$m\frac{d^2x}{dt^2} = -T - R = -\frac{\lambda x}{l} - k\dot{x}$$

$$0.1\frac{d^2x}{dt^2} + 0.2\frac{dx}{dt} + \frac{0.6}{1.2}x = 0$$

$$\frac{d^2x}{dt^2} + 2\frac{dx}{dt} + 5x = 0$$

The solution of this equation is found by substituting

$$x = e^{mt}$$

in the differential equation, giving

$$m^2 + 2m + 5 = 0.$$

Solving, $\quad m = \frac{-2 \pm \sqrt{4 - 20}}{2}$

$$= -1 \pm 2i$$

So $\quad x = Ae^{(-1+2i)t} + Be^{(-1-2i)t}$

$$\Rightarrow \quad x = e^{-t}(C\cos 2t + D\sin 2t)$$

Applying the conditions, at $t = 0$, $x = 0.2$ and $\dot{x} = 0.4$;

so $\quad 0.2 = C$

and, since

$$\dot{x} = -e^{-t}(C\cos 2t + D\sin 2t) + e^{-t}(-2C\sin 2t + 2D\cos 2t)$$

at $t = 0$,

$$0.4 = -C + 2D$$

Solving,

$$C = 0.2 \text{ and } D = 0.3$$

giving the complete solution for x as

$$x = e^{-t}(0.2\cos 2t + 0.3\sin 2t).$$

3

Worked example 3.6

A particle, of mass 3 kg, is suspended from a point, A, by an elastic string of natural length 2 m and modulus 60 N.
The particle is pulled vertically downwards until it is 3.25 m below A. It is then released from rest. Time, t s, is measured from the moment of release.
A resistive force, equal in magnitude to $18\dot{x}$ N, also acts on the particle, where x m is the extension of the string below the equilibrium position of the particle. In this question, take $g = 10\,\text{m s}^{-2}$.

(a) Show that the equation of motion of the particle is
$$\frac{d^2x}{dt^2} + 6\frac{dx}{dt} + 10x = 0.$$

(b) Show that, at time t,
$$x = \frac{\sqrt{10}}{4}e^{-3t}\cos(t - \alpha)$$
and state the value of α.

(c) Find the times at which the particle is at rest.

(d) Hence, show that the magnitude of the distances from the equilibrium position at which the particle is stationary from a sequence whose successive terms are in the ratio $e^{-3\pi}$.

Solution

(a) Let the extension of the string in equilibrium be e. Then applying Hooke's Law gives

$$3g = 60\frac{e}{2}$$
$$e = 1$$

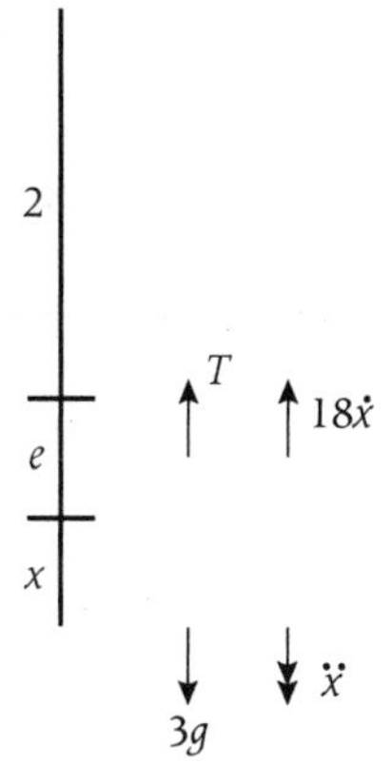

If x is the extension beyond the equilibrium position, then

$$T = \frac{60(x+e)}{2} = 30x + 30.$$

Remember that when x is increasing, that is when the particle is moving downwards, the air resistance will be acting to oppose motion, hence it is acting vertically upwards.
The air resistance mkv or $mk\dot{x}$ (remember $v = \dot{x}$) is thus acting **vertically upwards**.

Using $F = ma = m\ddot{x}$ vertically, with downwards defined as the positive, gives

$$3\ddot{x} = 3g - T - 18\dot{x}$$
$$= 3g - (30x + 30) - 18\dot{x}$$

$$3\ddot{x} + 18\dot{x} + 30x = 0$$

$$\frac{d^2x}{dt^2} + 6\frac{dx}{dt} + 10x = 0$$

(b) To solve $\dfrac{d^2x}{dt^2} + 6\dfrac{dx}{dt} + 10x = 0$, substitute $x = Ae^{nt}$

$$n^2 + 6n + 10 = 0$$

$$n = \frac{-6 \pm \sqrt{36 - 40}}{2} = -3 \pm i$$

$\therefore$ the solution is $x = e^{-3t}(A\cos t + B\sin t)$ [1]

When $t = 0$, $x = \dfrac{1}{4} \Rightarrow \dfrac{1}{4} = A$

Differentiating [1]

$$\frac{dx}{dt} = -3e^{-3t}(A\cos t + B\sin t) + e^{-3t}(-A\sin t + B\cos t)$$

When $t = 0$, $\dot{x} = 0 \Rightarrow 0 = -3A + B \Rightarrow B = \dfrac{3}{4}$

$$x = e^{-3t}\left(\frac{1}{4}\cos t + \frac{3}{4}\sin t\right) = \frac{\sqrt{10}}{4}e^{-3t}\cos(t - \alpha)$$

where $\tan\alpha = 3$ or $\alpha = 1.25^c$.

(c) The particle is at rest when $\dot{x} = 0$

$$\dot{x} = \frac{\sqrt{10}}{4}\left[-3e^{-3t}\cos(t-\alpha) - e^{-3t}\sin(t-\alpha)\right] = 0$$

$$\tan(t - \alpha) = -3$$

$$t = n\pi + \alpha - \alpha = n\pi$$

(d) At these values of t, the magnitude of the values of x are

$$\frac{\sqrt{10}}{4}\cos\alpha,\quad \frac{\sqrt{10}}{4}e^{-3\pi}\cos\alpha,\quad \frac{\sqrt{10}}{4}e^{-6\pi}\cos\alpha, \text{ etc.}$$

i.e. they form a geometric progression with common ratio $e^{-3\pi}$.

> The differential equation for damped motion will have solutions of the form
>
> $x = Ae^{m_1 t} + Be^{m_2 t}$ for heavy damping, when $k^2 - 4\omega^2 > 0$
>
> $x = (A + Bt)e^{\frac{k}{2}t}$ for critical damping, when $k^2 - 4\omega^2 = 0$
>
> $x = e^{-\frac{k}{2}t}\left(C\sin\dfrac{\alpha}{2}t + D\cos\dfrac{\alpha}{2}t\right)$ for light damping, when $k^2 - 4\omega^2 < 0$
>
> and where $\alpha^2 = 4\omega^2 - k^2$.

EXERCISE 3A

1 Solve the differential equations below that arise from damped harmonic motion. In each case state whether the damping is light, critical or heavy.

(a) $\dfrac{d^2x}{dt^2} + 7\dfrac{dx}{dt} + 6x = 0.$

(b) $\dfrac{d^2x}{dt^2} + 6\dfrac{dx}{dt} + 9x = 0.$

(c) $\dfrac{d^2x}{dt^2} + 7\dfrac{dx}{dt} + 12x = 0.$

(d) $\dfrac{d^2x}{dt^2} + 4\dfrac{dx}{dt} + 13x = 0.$

(e) $\dfrac{d^2x}{dt^2} + 5\dfrac{dx}{dt} + 8.5x = 0.$

(f) $\dfrac{d^2x}{dt^2} + 5\dfrac{dx}{dt} + 6.25x = 0.$

2 (a) Find x when $\dfrac{d^2x}{dt^2} + 3\dfrac{dx}{dt} + 2x = 0$ given that $x = 0$ and $\dfrac{dx}{dt} = 5$ when $t = 0$.

(b) Find x when $\dfrac{d^2x}{dt^2} + 11\dfrac{dx}{dt} + 10x = 0$ given that $x = 3$ and $\dfrac{dx}{dt} = 0$ when $t = 0$.

(c) Find x when $\dfrac{d^2x}{dt^2} + 4\dfrac{dx}{dt} + 4x = 0$ given that $x = 8$ and $\dfrac{dx}{dt} = 0$ when $t = 0$.

(d) Find x when $\dfrac{d^2x}{dt^2} + 5\dfrac{dx}{dt} + 7x = 0$ given that $x = 3$ and $\dfrac{dx}{dt} = 0$ when $t = 0$.

(e) Find x when $\dfrac{d^2x}{dt^2} + 2\dfrac{dx}{dt} + 6x = 0$ given that $x = 0$ and $\dfrac{dx}{dt} = 4$ when $t = 0$.

(f) Find x when $\dfrac{d^2x}{dt^2} + \dfrac{dx}{dt} + 3x = 0$ given that $x = 2$ and $\dfrac{dx}{dt} = 0$ when $t = 0$.

Also state whether the motion in each of the above cases would involve heavy, critical or light damping.

3 The three points A, O, B, in that order, are in a straight line on a smooth horizontal table, with $AO = OB = 2a$. One end of each of two light elastic strings of natural length a and modulus $5mn^2a$ (where n is a positive constant) is attached to

a particle, P, of mass m, and the other ends of the strings are fastened to A and B respectively. The particle moves along the line AB and is subject to a resistive force of magnitude $2mn$ times its speed. Assuming that both strings remain taut, show that the displacement, x, of P from O at time t, will satisfy

$$\frac{d^2x}{dt^2} + 2n\frac{dx}{dt} + 10n^2x = 0.$$

Given that, at $t = 0$, $x = a$ and $\frac{dx}{dt} = -10na$, find x at any subsequent time t. Draw a sketch graph showing the behaviour of the speed of the particle with time for $0 \leqslant t \leqslant \frac{\pi}{2n}$. [A]

4 A particle, P, of mass m, is attached to one end of a light spring of modulus $2mn^2a$ and natural length a, where n is a constant. The other end of the spring is attached to a fixed point O. The particle is in equilibrium at a point B directly below O, and at time $t = 0$ an impulse is applied to P so that it starts to move down with speed u. The particle is also subject to a resistive force of magnitude $2mn$ times its speed. Show that x, its downward displacement from B at time t, satisfies

$$\frac{d^2x}{dt^2} + 2n\frac{dx}{dt} + 2n^2x = 0.$$

Find x in terms of n, u and t.
The particle first comes to instantaneous rest at a point Q_1 below B and then moves upwards through B, coming next to instantaneous rest at a point Q_2 above B and then moving downwards through B. Find $\frac{BQ_2}{BQ_1}$. [A]

5 The diagram shows a model of a car suspension system. A mass, M, is supported on a vertically mounted spring, of stiffness k, fixed at its lower end. The mass is also attached to a piston which moves in a fluid-filled cylinder, so that the motion of the mass is resisted by a force of magnitude $2b$ times the momentum of the mass ($b > 0$).

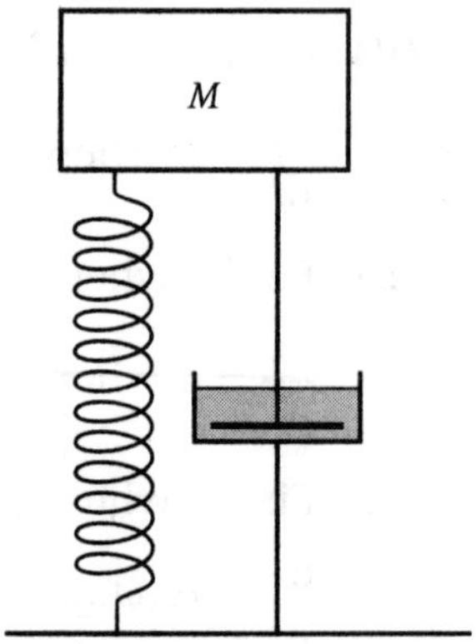

(a) When the system is in equilibrium, show that the spring is compressed by an amount l, where

$$l = \frac{Mg}{k}.$$

(b) The mass is now disturbed from its equilibrium position. Let x be the displacement of the mass from its equilibrium position, measured vertically downwards. Write down the equation of motion of the mass and show that it may be expressed as

$$\frac{d^2x}{dt^2} + 2b\frac{dx}{dt} + \omega^2x = 0, \text{ where } \omega^2 = \frac{k}{M}.$$

(c) (i) Show that, when $b > \omega$, the general solution of the equation from **(b)** is

$$x = e^{-bt}(Ae^{\lambda t} + Be^{-\lambda t}), \text{ where } \lambda = \sqrt{b^2 - \omega^2},$$

and sketch a typical graph of the solution.

(ii) Find the general solution when $b < \omega$ and sketch a typical graph of the solution.

(iii) Which of the cases $b < \omega$ and $b > \omega$ would be more appropriate for a car suspension system? Give a reason for your answer.

3.2 Forced harmonic motion

Having analysed the effect that a natural damping factor has on harmonic motion, we will now take the analysis of vibrating systems another step by including an external forcing function $F(t)$ on the system.

Consider a particle lying on a smooth horizontal plane, and which is attached to one end, B, of a spring. The other end of the spring, A, may be attached to a fixed point. The external force may be either applied to the particle, for example, by means of an electromagnetic force, or it may be applied to the end, A, of the spring by means of movement of the point to which A is attached.

In either of these cases, the forces acting on the particle at B are:

- T, tension in the spring, assumed to obey Hooke's Law,
- R, a force which is resistant to motion and proportional to velocity, that is, $R = mkv = mk\dot{x}$,
- $F(t)$ which is a forcing function.

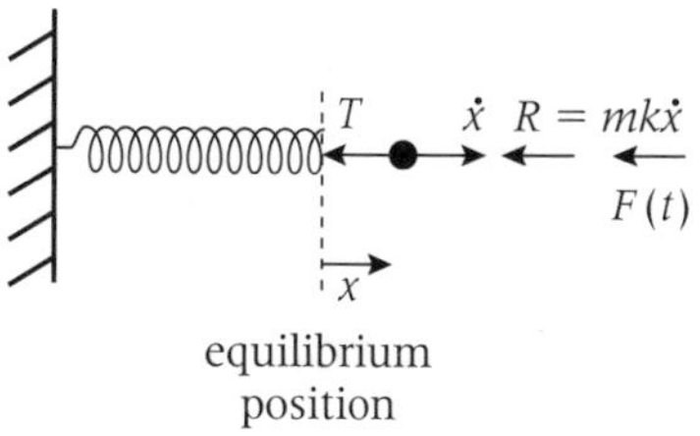

Using $F = ma = m\ddot{x}$, the equation of motion is,

$$m\frac{d^2x}{dt^2} = F(t) - R - T.$$

Remember that if x is the movement of the particle from its initial position at B in the direction away from A, $\dot{x}$ and $\ddot{x}$ are both positive in the direction away from A.

Writing $f(t) = \dfrac{F(t)}{m}$, so that $f(t)$ is the forcing function per unit mass and using $T = \dfrac{\lambda x}{l}$ gives,

$$m\frac{d^2x}{dt^2} = mf(t) - mk\frac{dx}{dt} - \frac{\lambda x}{l}$$

or $\dfrac{d^2x}{dt^2} + k\dfrac{dx}{dt} + \omega^2 x = f(t)$, where again $\omega^2 = \dfrac{\lambda}{lm}$

The general solution of the differential equation

$$\frac{d^2x}{dt^2} + k\frac{dx}{dt} + \omega^2 x = f(t)$$

is made up of two parts, namely,

$$x = x_c(t) + x_p(t)$$

where $x_c(t)$ is the general solution of the associated homogeneous equation (i.e. the right-hand side of the equation is zero) which is

$$\frac{d^2x}{dt^2} + k\frac{dx}{dt} + \omega^2 x = 0$$

and $x_p(t)$ is one particular solution of the full equation.

From the previous section you discovered how to find $x_c(t)$ which is the complementary function, or CF.

The particular solution, $x_p(t)$, depends on the forcing function $f(t)$.

The three types of forcing function, $f(t)$, which we will consider at Advanced level are:

- polynomial,
- exponential,
- trigonometric.

Polynomial forcing functions

If $f(t)$ is a polynomial of degree n, then the particular solution will also be a polynomial of degree n. For example, if $f(t)$ is of the form $3t^2 + 7t + 5$ then the particular solution will be of the form $at^2 + bt + c$.

Worked example 3.7

By finding

(a) the complementary function, and **(b)** the particular solution,

solve the equation: $\frac{d^2x}{dt^2} + 5\frac{dx}{dt} + 6x = 12.$

Solution

(a) For the complementary function:

$$\frac{d^2x}{dt^2} + 5\frac{dx}{dt} + 6x = 0,$$

Substituting $x = Ae^{mt}$

$m^2 + 5m + 6 = 0$
$(m + 2)(m + 3) = 0$
$m = -2, -3$
CF is $x = Ae^{-2t} + Be^{-3t}$

(b) For the particular solution, $f(t)$ is a polynomial of degree 0, hence we need only consider $x = c$.

Substituting $x = c$ into $\frac{d^2x}{dt^2} + 5\frac{dx}{dt} + 6x = 12$,
gives $6c = 12$

$c = 2$

The particular solution is $x = 2$.
The general solution is $x = Ae^{-2t} + Be^{-3t} + 2$.

You will notice that as t tends to infinity, x tends to 2.

Worked example 3.8

Find the solution of $\frac{d^2x}{dt^2} + 5\frac{dx}{dt} + 6x = 3 + 18t^2$, given that when $t = 0$, $x = 0$ and $\frac{dx}{dt} = 2$.

Solution

For the CF, use $\frac{d^2x}{dt^2} + 5\frac{dx}{dt} + 6x = 0$.

As above, in Worked example 3.7, substituting $x = Ae^{mt}$ gives the CF to be $x = Ae^{-2t} + Be^{-3t}$.

To find the particular solution, substitute $x = a + bt + ct^2$ into the equation $\frac{d^2x}{dt^2} + 5\frac{dx}{dt} + 6x = 3 + 18t^2$

$2c + 5(b + 2ct) + 6(a + bt + ct^2) = 3 + 18t^2$

Equating coefficients of t^2: $6c = 18$

$c = 3$

Equating coefficients of t: $10c + 6b = 0$

$b = -5$

Let $t = 0$: $2c + 5b + 6a = 3$

$a = \frac{11}{3}$

The particular solution is $x = \frac{11}{3} - 5t + 3t^2$.

The general solution is $x = Ae^{-2t} + Be^{-3t} + \frac{11}{3} - 5t + 3t^2$.

The initial conditions can be used to determine the values of A and B.

When $t = 0$, $x = 0$,

$$0 = A + B + \frac{11}{3}$$

$$\frac{dx}{dt} = -2Ae^{-2t} - 3Be^{-3t} - 5 + 6t$$

When $t = 0$, $\dfrac{dx}{dt} = 2$,

$$2 = -2A - 3B - 5$$
$$7 = -2A - 4B$$

From the simultaneous equations above,

$$B = \frac{1}{6},\ A = -\frac{23}{6}$$

Hence, the general solution is

$$x = -\frac{23}{6}e^{-2t} + \frac{1}{6}e^{-3t} + \frac{11}{3} - 5t + 3t^2.$$

Exponential forcing functions

> If $f(x)$ is an exponential function, e.g., $5e^{-7t}$, then the particular solution is of the same form, i.e., Ce^{-7t}.

Worked example 3.9

Find the general solution of the differential equation

$$\frac{d^2x}{dt^2} + 5\frac{dx}{dt} + 6x = 5e^{-4t}.$$

Solution

For the CF use $\dfrac{d^2x}{dt^2} + 5\dfrac{dx}{dt} + 6x = 0$.

As in the examples above, substituting $x = Ae^{mt}$ gives the CF to be $x = Ae^{-2t} + Be^{-3t}$.

To find the particular solution, substitute $x = Ce^{-4t}$ into

$$\frac{d^2x}{dt^2} + 5\frac{dx}{dt} + 6x = 5e^{-4t}$$

which gives

$$16Ce^{-4t} - 20Ce^{-4t} + 6Ce^{-4t} = 5Ce^{-4t}$$
$$2C = 5$$

So the PS is $x = \frac{5}{2}e^{-4t}$.

The general solution is $x = Ae^{-2t} + Be^{-3t} + \frac{5}{2}e^{-4t}$.

Trigonometric forcing functions

> If $f(x)$ is a trigonometric function such as $3\sin\omega t$, then the particular solution will be of the form $C\sin\omega t + D\cos\omega t$.

Worked example 3.10

Find the general solution of the differential equation

$$\frac{d^2x}{dt^2} + 5\frac{dx}{dt} + 6x = 4\sin 5t.$$

Solution

The CF is $x = Ae^{-2t} + Be^{-3t}$ (as in the examples above).

Caution: If we simply consider $x = C\sin 5t$ as the particular solution, because there is only a $\sin 2t$ term on the right-hand side, we obtain:

$$\frac{dx}{dt} = 5C\cos 5t \qquad \frac{d^2x}{dt^2} = -25C\sin 5t$$

When substituted into $\frac{d^2x}{dt^2} + 5\frac{dx}{dt} + 6x = 4\sin 5t$, this will give

$$-25C\sin 5t + 5 \times 5C\cos 5t + 6C\sin 5t = 4\sin 5t,$$

which includes only one term in $\cos 5t \left(\text{from } \frac{dx}{dt}\right)$.

This means that this equation cannot be solved. Hence the particular solution used **must** contain **both** $\sin 5t$ **and** $\cos 5t$ terms.

Assume that the particular solution is of the form

$$x = C\sin 5t + D\cos 5t$$
$$\frac{dx}{dt} = 5C\cos 5t - 5D\sin 5t$$
$$\frac{d^2x}{dt^2} = -25C\sin 5t - 25D\cos 5t$$

Substituting into $\frac{d^2x}{dt^2} + 5\frac{dx}{dt} + 6x = 4\sin 5t$ gives

$$-25C\sin 5t - 25D\cos 5t + 25C\cos 5t - 25D\sin 5t$$
$$+ 6C\sin 5t + 6D\cos t = 4\sin 5t$$

Equate coefficients of $\sin 5t$: $-19C - 25D = 4$ [1]

Equate coefficients of $\cos 5t$: $-19D + 25C = 0$ [2]

Multiplying [1] by 19: $-361C - 475D = 76$ [3]

Multiplying [2] by 25: $-475D + 625C = 0$ [4]

Subtracting [4] from [3] $-986C = 76$

$$C = -\frac{38}{493}$$

$$\therefore \quad D = \frac{25}{19}C = -\frac{50}{493}$$

So the particular solution is

$$x = -\frac{38}{493}\sin 5t - \frac{50}{493}\cos 5t$$

and the general solution is

$$x = Ae^{-2t} + Be^{-3t} - \frac{38}{493}\sin 5t - \frac{50}{493}\cos 5t.$$

Worked example 3.11

Solve the differential equation

$$\frac{d^2x}{dt^2} + 5\frac{dx}{dt} + 6x = 7e^{-2t}$$

given that $x = 0$ and $\frac{dx}{dt} = 4$ when $t = 0$.

Solution

As in the examples above the CF is $x = Ae^{-2t} + Be^{-3t}$.

To find the particular solution let $x = Cte^{-2t}$.

Note that Cte^{-2t} is used here because Ce^{-2t} is already used as part of the CF.

$$\frac{dx}{dt} = Ce^{-2t} - 2Cte^{-2t}$$

$$\frac{d^2x}{dt^2} = -2Ce^{-2t} - 2Ce^{-2t} + 4Cte^{-2t}$$

Substituting into $\frac{d^2x}{dt^2} + 5\frac{dx}{dt} + 6x = 7e^{-2t}$ gives

$$-2Ce^{-2t} - 2Ce^{-2t} + 4Cte^{-2t} + 5(Ce^{-2t} - 2Cte^{-2t}) + 6Cte^{-2t} = 7e^{-2t}$$

(Note that the t terms should cancel at this stage.)

$$Ce^{-2t} = 7e^{-2t}$$
$$C = 7$$

The particular solution is $x = 7te^{-2t}$ and the general solution is

$$x = Ae^{-2t} + Be^{-3t} + 7te^{-2t}.$$

At this stage, after adding the complementary function and the particular solution, the boundary conditions can be used to determine the values of the arbitrary constants.

$$x = 0 \text{ when } t = 0 \Rightarrow 0 = A + B,$$

$$\frac{dx}{dt} = -2Ae^{-2t} - 3Be^{-3t} + 7e^{-2t} - 14te^{-2t}$$

$$\frac{dx}{dt} = 4 \text{ when } t = 0$$

$$4 = -2A - 3B + 7$$
$$-3 = 2A - 3B$$
$$\text{since } 0 = A + B$$
$$A = -\tfrac{3}{5},\ B = \tfrac{3}{5}$$

The solution is $x = (7t - \frac{3}{5})e^{-2t} + \frac{3}{5}e^{-3t}$.

Worked example 3.12

Find the general solution of this differential equation

$$\ddot{x} + 16x = 4\cos 4t.$$

Solution

To find the complementary function, substitute $x = Ae^{mt}$ and simplify to give

$$m^2 + 16 = 0,$$
$$m = \pm 4i$$

The CF is $x = A\cos 4t + B\sin 4t$.

Note that for the particular solution we need once again to use terms in $t\cos 4t$ and $t\sin 4t$, since the CF has already used the terms $\cos 4t$ and $\sin 4t$.

So the PS will be of the form

$$x = Ct\cos 4t + Dt\sin 4t$$
$$\dot{x} = C\cos 4t - 4Ct\sin 4t + D\sin 4t + 4Dt\cos 4t$$
$$\ddot{x} = -4C\sin 4t - 4C\sin 4t - 16Ct\cos 4t + 4D\cos 4t + 4D\cos 4t - 16Dt\sin 4t$$

Substituting into the differential equation, $\ddot{x} + 16x = 4\cos 4t$, gives

$$-8C\sin 4t - 16Ct\cos 4t + 8D\cos 4t - 16Dt\sin 4t + 16Ct\cos 4t + 16Dt\sin 4t = 4\cos 4t$$

Simplifying, equating sine and cosine terms, and remembering that the terms in t should cancel, gives

$$-8C = 0$$
$$C = 0$$
$$8D = 4$$
$$D = \tfrac{1}{2}$$

So the PS is $x = \frac{1}{2}t\sin 4t$ and the general solution is

$$x = A\sin 4t + B\cos 4t + \frac{t}{2}\sin 4t.$$

Worked example 3.13

A vibrating system is subject to a forcing function, but has no damping. The motion of the system is modelled by the differential equation below.

$$\frac{d^2x}{dt^2} + \omega^2 x = \cos pt$$

with initial conditions $x = a$, $\dot{x} = 0$ when $t = 0$, and

(a) $p \neq \omega$, **(b)** $p = \omega$

In both cases, describe the motion.

Solution

The solution for x is given by

$$x(t) = x_c(t) + x_p(t)$$

where $x_c(t)$ is the general solution of

$$\frac{d^2x}{dt^2} + \omega^2 x = 0.$$

As you have seen earlier, this has the general solution

$$x_c(t) = A\cos\omega t + B\sin\omega t.$$

(a) For a particular solution, try

$$x_p(t) = a\sin pt + b\cos pt.$$

Thus $\dfrac{dx_p}{dt} = ap\cos pt - bp\sin pt$

$$\frac{d^2x_p}{dt^2} = -ap^2\sin pt - bp^2\cos pt$$

and substituting in the differential equation gives

$$-ap^2\sin pt - bp^2\cos pt + \omega^2(a\sin pt + b\cos pt) = \cos pt$$
$$a(\omega^2 - p^2)\sin pt + b(\omega^2 - p^2)\cos pt = \cos pt$$

To satisfy these equations, you must take

$$[\sin pt] \quad a(\omega^2 - p^2) = 0$$
$$[\cos pt] \quad b(\omega^2 - p^2) = 1$$

Since $\omega \neq p$, $a = 0$ and $b = \dfrac{1}{\omega^2 - p^2}$, giving

$$x_p(t) = \frac{1}{(\omega^2 - p^2)}\cos pt$$

and general solution

$$x(t) = A\cos\omega t + B\sin\omega t + \frac{1}{(\omega^2 - p^2)}\cos pt.$$

The initial condition gives

$$x = a \text{ at } t = 0 \Rightarrow a = A + \frac{1}{(\omega^2 - p^2)}$$

and since

$$\dot{x}(t) = -A\omega\sin\omega t + B\omega\cos\omega t - \frac{p}{(\omega^2 - p^2)}\sin pt,$$

at $t = 0$, $\dot{x} = 0$, giving $0 = B$.

So, the complete solution is given by

$$x(t) = \left(a - \frac{1}{(\omega^2 - p^2)}\right)\cos\omega t + \frac{1}{(\omega^2 - p^2)}\cos pt.$$

This predicts an oscillating solution for $x(t)$, since it combines two oscillating functions.

A graph of x against t is shown below for the case when $p = 2$, $\omega = 4$ and $a = 1$.

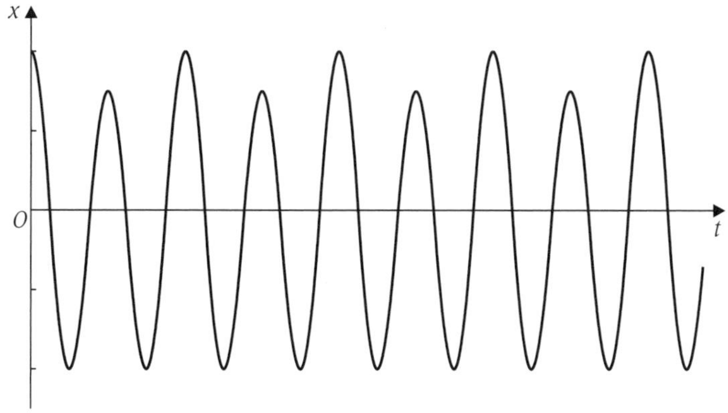

(b) You can see that when $p = \omega$, the solution found above breaks down. So a different particular solution of

$$\frac{d^2x}{dt^2} + \omega^2 x = \cos \omega t$$

is required.

A possibility for the particular solution is $a \sin \omega t + b \cos \omega t$ but you will realise that this is in fact the complementary solution, and so cannot be used.
As you have found on a number of occasions, when the function to be used as a particular solution has already been used in the complementary function, you must multiply the intended particular solution by t.
Thus we can use $at \sin \omega t + bt \cos \omega t$ to obtain the particular integral.

Hence,

$$\frac{dx_p}{dt} = a \sin \omega t + a\omega t \cos \omega t + b \cos \omega t - bt\omega \sin \omega t$$
$$= (a - bt\omega) \sin \omega t + (a\omega t + b) \cos \omega t$$

and

$$\frac{d^2x_p}{dt^2} = -b\omega \sin \omega t + \omega(a - bt\omega) \cos \omega t$$
$$+ a\omega \cos \omega t - \omega(a\omega t + b) \sin \omega t$$
$$= -\omega(a\omega t + 2b) \sin \omega t + \omega(2a - bt\omega) \cos \omega t$$

Substituting in the differential equation gives

$$-\omega(a\omega t + 2b) \sin \omega t + \omega(2a - bt\omega) \cos \omega t$$
$$+ \omega^2(at \sin \omega t + bt \cos \omega t) = \cos \omega t$$
$$\Rightarrow \quad -2b\omega \sin \omega t + 2a\omega \cos \omega t = \cos \omega t$$

This equation is satisfied by

$$2a\omega = 1 \text{ and } 2b\omega = 0$$

$$\Rightarrow \quad a = \frac{1}{2\omega},\ b = 0$$

and $x_p(t) = \dfrac{t}{2\omega}\sin\omega t$.

The general solution is given by

$$x(t) = A\cos\omega t + B\sin\omega t + \frac{t}{2\omega}\sin\omega t.$$

Applying the initial conditions,

$$x = a,\ t = 0 \Rightarrow a = A$$

and, since

$$\dot{x}(t) = -A\omega\sin\omega t + B\omega\cos\omega t + \frac{1}{2\omega}\sin\omega t + \frac{t}{2}\cos\omega t$$

at $t = 0$, $\dot{x} = 0$ giving

$$0 = B\omega \Rightarrow B = 0.$$

So the complete solution is

$$x(t) = a\cos\omega t + \frac{t}{2\omega}\sin\omega t.$$

Again this has oscillating behaviour but note the t multiplier which will give an increasing amplitude, as shown in the graph below.

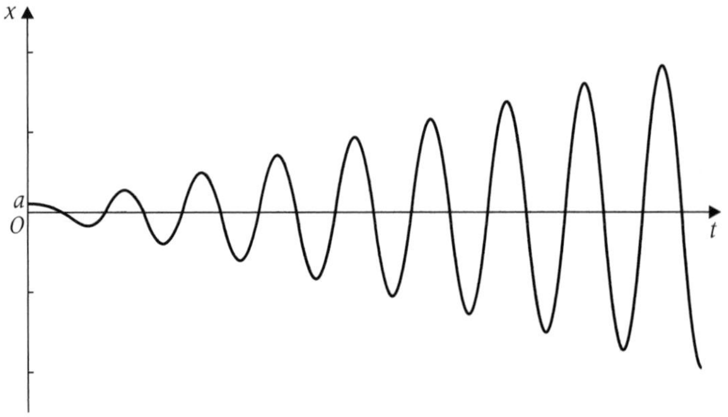

This is an example of resonance.

> If a system is allowed to oscillate freely, it will do so at what is called its natural frequency. If the forcing function has the same frequency as the natural frequency, then resonance takes place.

3

Worked example 3.14

The ends of a light, uniform elastic string are fixed to two points, A and B, distance $6a$ apart on a smooth, horizontal plane. The string is of natural length $3a$ and modulus of elasticity $2am$. A particle, of mass m, is attached to the string at P, where $AP = 2a$. In this position the particle is in equilibrium.

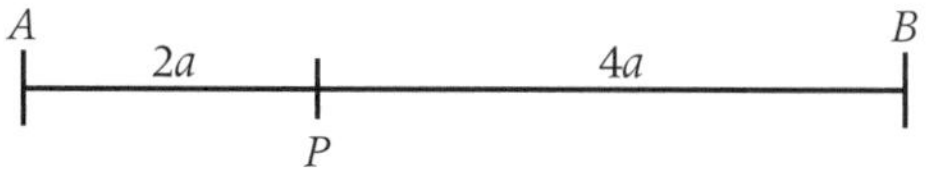

The particle is moved a distance a towards A and then released from rest at time $t = 0$.
The motion of the particle is resisted by a force of magnitude $2m\dfrac{dx}{dt}$, where x is the distance of the particle from its equilibrium position at time t.

(a) Show that x satisfies $\dfrac{d^2x}{dt^2} + 2\dfrac{dx}{dt} + 3x = 0$.

(b) Find the general solution of this equation.

(c) A forcing function, $6mae^{-3t}$, in the direction towards A is now applied to the particle so that the equation of motion becomes

$$\frac{d^2x}{dt^2} + 2\frac{dx}{dt} + 3x = 6ae^{-3t}.$$

The particle is again released from rest at time $t = 0$ when it is a distance a from A.

Show that $x = ae^{-3t} + \dfrac{3a}{\sqrt{2}}e^{-t}\sin\sqrt{2}t$.

Solution

(a) The equilibrium position O is $2a$ from A.
Extension in AP (when particle is x from O) is $a - x$.
Extension in PB is $2a + x$.

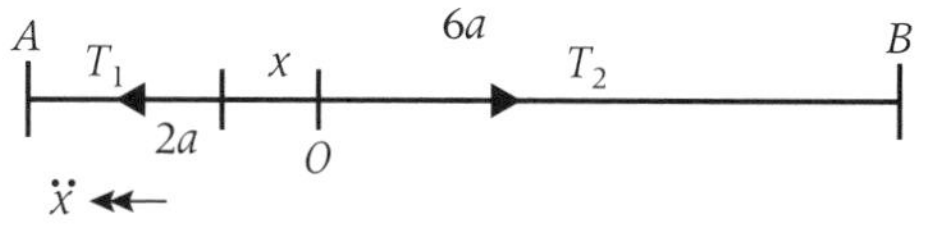

$$T_1 = \frac{\lambda x}{l} = \frac{2am(a-x)}{a}$$

$$T_2 = \frac{2am(2a+x)}{2a}$$

Using $F = ma$ for the particle

$$m\frac{d^2x}{dt^2} = T_1 - T_2 - 2m\frac{dx}{dt}$$

$$= 2m(a-x) - m(2a+x) - 2m\frac{dx}{dt}$$

$$\frac{d^2x}{dt^2} + 2\frac{dx}{dt} + 3x = 0$$

(b) Substituting $x = Ae^{mt}$, $m^2 + 2m + 3 = 0$

$$m = \frac{-2 \pm \sqrt{4 - 12}}{2} = -1 \pm i\sqrt{2}$$

The general solution is $x = e^{-t}(A \cos \sqrt{2}t + B \sin \sqrt{2}t)$.

(c) CF is $x = e^{-t}(A \cos \sqrt{2}t + B \sin \sqrt{2}t)$

PS is $x = ce^{-3t}$

Substituting into the differential equation gives

$$9ce^{-3t} - 6ce^{-3t} + 3ce^{-3t} = 6ae^{-3t}$$

$$c = a$$

PS is $x = ae^{-3t}$

The solution is $x = ae^{-3t} + e^{-t}(A \cos \sqrt{2}t + B \sin \sqrt{2}t)$.

When $t = 0$, $x = a \Rightarrow a = a + A \Rightarrow A = 0$

$$\frac{dx}{dt} = -3ae^{-3t} - e^{-t}B \sin \sqrt{2}t + \sqrt{2}e^{-t}B \cos \sqrt{2}t$$

$$= 0 \text{ when } t = 0 \Rightarrow 0 = -3a + \sqrt{2}B$$

$$B = \frac{3a}{\sqrt{2}}$$

The solution is $x = ae^{-3t} + \frac{3a}{\sqrt{2}}e^{-t} \sin \sqrt{2}t$.

EXERCISE 3B

1 Solve the differential equations below:

(a) $\frac{d^2x}{dt^2} + 7\frac{dx}{dt} + 6x = 12$, **(b)** $\frac{d^2x}{dt^2} + 6\frac{dx}{dt} + 9x = 4 + t^2$,

(c) $\frac{d^2x}{dt^2} + 6\frac{dx}{dt} + 5x = 6e^{-2t}$, **(d)** $\frac{d^2x}{dt^2} + 4\frac{dx}{dt} + 13x = 5e^{-t}$,

(e) $\frac{d^2x}{dt^2} + 9x = \cos 2t + 3 \sin 2t$, **(f)** $\frac{d^2x}{dt^2} + 49x = 4 \cos 7t$.

2 (a) Find x when $\frac{d^2x}{dt^2} + 2\frac{dx}{dt} + 2x = 8$ given that $x = 0$ and $\frac{dx}{dt} = 4$ when $t = 0$.

(b) Find x when $\frac{d^2x}{dt^2} + 6\frac{dx}{dt} + 8x = 6e^{-2t}$ given that $x = 5$ and $\frac{dx}{dt} = 0$ when $t = 0$.

(c) Find x when $\frac{d^2x}{dt^2} + 10\frac{dx}{dt} + 25x = 2e^{-5t}$ given that $x = 5$ and $\frac{dx}{dt} = 0$ when $t = 0$.

(d) Find x when $\frac{d^2x}{dt^2} + x = 2e^{-t}$ given that $x = 5$ and $\frac{dx}{dt} = 0$ when $t = 0$.

(e) Find x when $\frac{d^2x}{dt^2} + 9x = 5e^{-3t}$ given that $x = 0$ and $\frac{dx}{dt} = 3$ when $t = 0$.

(f) Find x when $\frac{d^2x}{dt^2} + 2\frac{dx}{dt} + 3x = \cos t$ given that $x = 1$ and $\frac{dx}{dt} = 0$ when $t = 0$.

3

3 Solve the differential equation of forced harmonic motion when

$$\frac{d^2x}{dt^2} + 4\frac{dx}{dt} + 3x = f(t), \text{ and}$$

(a) $f(t) = c$, a constant,

(b) $f(t) = e^t$,

(c) $f(t) = e^{-t}$.

In each case, find the behaviour of x for large t.

4 Solve the equation of harmonic motion

$$\frac{d^2x}{dt^2} + 4x = \sin pt; \; x = a, \; \dot{x} = 0 \text{ at } t = 0, \text{ when:}$$

(a) $p = 1$, **(b)** $p = 2$.

5 A body, of mass m, which is suspended on the end of an elastic spring, moves such that its vertical displacement, x, from its equilibrium position is given by

$$\ddot{x} + 4n^2x = an^2 \cos nt,$$

where a and n are positive constants. Given that $x = 0$ and $\dot{x} = 0$ when $t = 0$, find the displacement at any time t. [A]

6 A light spring, AB, of natural length a and modulus mn^2a lies straight and slack on a rough horizontal table. A particle, of mass m, is attached to the spring at B. The coefficient of friction between the table and the particle is μ.

Initially the particle is at rest and the end A is then made to move with constant speed u in the direction BA.

Find the extension in the spring when the particle starts to move.

At a time t after the particle starts to move, its distance from its original position is denoted by x.

Show that, while x is increasing,

$$\frac{d^2x}{dt^2} + n^2x = n^2 ut.$$

Find x at time t and also the maximum speed of the particle.

[A]

7 A particle of mass m moves along the x-axis and is attracted towards the origin, O, by a force of magnitude $5m\omega^2$ times its distance from O, where ω is a constant. The particle is resisted by a force of magnitude $4m\omega$ times its speed. No other forces act. Write down the differential equation for the particle's displacement, x, along the line from O, and show that, at time t,

$$x = e^{-2\omega t}(A \cos \omega t + B \sin \omega t)$$

where A and B are constants. [A]

8 A particle, of mass m, moves along the x-axis and is attracted towards the fixed origin, O, by a force of magnitude $5m\omega^2|x|$, where ω is a constant. In addition, the motion of the particle is resisted by a force of magnitude $4m\omega v$, where v is the speed of the particle at time t. Write down an equation of motion of the particle and hence show that, at any time t, $x = Ce^{-2\omega t} \cos(\omega t + \phi)$, where C and ϕ are constants.

Given that, at $t = 0$, $x = 3a$ and the particle is moving towards O with speed $2a\omega$, where a is a constant, find C and ϕ.

Sketch the graph of x against t, paying particular attention to the behaviour of x near $t = 0$ and as t becomes large. [A]

9 At time t, a particle, of mass m, is moving along the x-axis in the direction Ox. The particle is subject to a force of attraction towards O of magnitude $m\omega^2 x$ (where ω is a constant) and a forcing function $mf(t)$ away from O. Show that x, the distance of the particle from O in the positive direction, satisfies

$$\frac{d^2x}{dt^2} + \omega^2 x = f(t).$$

(a) Find the general solution for x when
(i) $f(t) = 0$, **(ii)** $f(t) = a \sin \omega t$ (a is a constant).

(b) In **(a) (ii)** the particle is initially at rest at the origin.
(i) Find x in terms of ω, a and t.
(ii) Give a sketch of the solution curve $x = x(t)$ and describe its main characteristics. [A]

10 One end of an elastic spring, of modulus of elasticity $18mn^2a$ and natural length a, is attached to a particle, P, of mass m. The other end is fastened to a point, O, on a horizontal table. The particle is free to move on the table in the line OP. At time t there is a force $9mn^2ae^{-3nt}$ acting on P in the sense from O to P and the motion of P is opposed by a frictional force of magnitude $6mn$ times its speed. Show that x, the extension of the spring, satisfies the differential equation

$$\frac{d^2x}{dt^2} + 6n\frac{dx}{dt} + 18n^2x = 9n^2ae^{-3nt}.$$

Given that at $t = 0$, $x = 0$ and $\dfrac{dx}{dt} = 0$, find x in terms of a, n and t and show that x never becomes negative. [A]

11 A particle, of mass m, is moving along a straight line and is attracted towards a fixed point, O, by a force $2m\omega^2x$, where x is the distance of the particle from O at time t and ω is a constant. In addition the motion of the particle is resisted by a force of magnitude $2m\omega\dot{x}$, where $\dot{x}$ is the speed of the particle at time t. Write down a differential equation to determine the motion of the particle and hence show that

$$x = Ce^{-\omega t}\cos(\omega t + \alpha),$$

where C and α are constants.

Given that at $t = 0$, $x = a$ and $\dot{x} = (\sqrt{3} - 1)a\omega$, where a is a constant, find C and α. Also find the times at which the particle is instantaneously at rest.

Sketch the graph of x against t, showing clearly the behaviour of x as t becomes large. [A]

12 [In this question take g to be $10\,\text{m}\,\text{s}^{-2}$.]

A particle, P, is attached to one end of a light elastic spring of natural length 0.5 m. The other end of the spring is held at a fixed point, A, and the particle hangs in equilibrium at the point B directly below A, where $AB = 0.525$ m. The equilibrium is disturbed by the upper end of the spring being made to oscillate in a vertical line so that, at time t s after the motion has been started, the downward displacement of the upper end of the spring from A is

$$0.02\sin 10t\ \text{m}.$$

Show that x m, the downward displacement of P from B at time t s, satisfies

$$\ddot{x} + 400x = 8\sin 10t.$$

Find x in terms of t. [A]

13 A particle moves in a straight line such that its displacement from a fixed point, O, at time t is given by

$$x = a\cos(\omega t - \phi)$$

where a, ω and ϕ are positive constants. It is observed that the period of the motion is 16 s and that at a certain time the particle is 5 m from O and that 4 s later it is still on the same side of O but 12 m from O. Find a, ω and ϕ.

Show that after a further 4 s the particle is on the other side of O and at a distance 5 m from O. Find the speed and acceleration of the particle in this position and state whether it is travelling towards or away from O. Also, find the time which elapses before the particle next passes through this position. [A]

14 A particle, of mass m, is attached to one end of a light spring of natural length a and modulus $5m\omega^2a$, where $\omega > 0$. The other end of the spring is attached to a fixed point O on a horizontal plane. At time $t = 0$, the particle is released from rest at a point A on the plane, where $OA = 3a$.

Given that the particle experiences a resistance to motion of magnitude $2m\omega$ times its speed, together with a driving force $10m\omega^2 a \cos \omega t$ in the direction OA, show that the extension, x, of the spring beyond its natural length at time t satisfies the equation

$$\ddot{x} + 2\omega\dot{x} + 5\omega^2 x = 10\omega^2 a \cos \omega t.$$

Find x in terms of a and ωt and show that for large values of t the motion of the particle is approximately simple harmonic with amplitude $\sqrt{5}a$. [A]

15

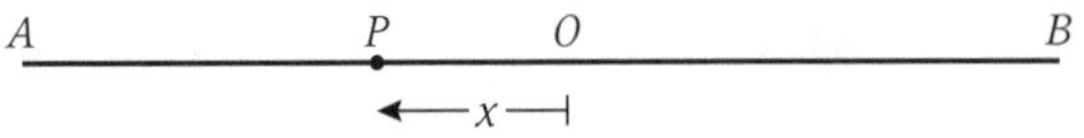

The diagram shows an elastic string of natural length 2 m and modulus of elasticity 5 N stretched between two points, A and B, at a distance 4 m apart on a smooth horizontal plane. O is the midpoint of AB. A particle, P, of mass 1 kg, attached to the midpoint of the string, is pulled towards A through a distance of $\frac{1}{3}$ m and released from rest at time $t = 0$. A resistive force, equal in magnitude to twice the velocity, and a force given by $3e^{-t}$ in the direction towards A, also act on the particle during the subsequent motion.

Show that the equation of motion of the particle is

$$\frac{d^2x}{dt^2} + 2\frac{dx}{dt} + 10x = 3e^{-t}$$

where x is the displacement of the particle from O towards A.

Solve this equation to find x at time t. [A]

Key point summary

1 We will often use the abbreviations p 41

$$\dot{x} = \frac{dx}{dt} \text{ and } \ddot{x} = \frac{d^2x}{dt^2} \text{ in the examples in this chapter.}$$

2 The solutions of the differential equation p 43

$\frac{d^2x}{dt^2} + k\frac{dx}{dt} + \omega^2 x = 0$, which models damped motion, are of the form $x = Ae^{mt}$, where

$m = \frac{-k \pm \sqrt{k^2 - 4\omega^2}}{2}$. The number, and type of solutions of this quadratic equation depend on the value of $k^2 - 4\omega^2$.

3 The differential equation for damped motion will have solutions of the form p 54

$x = Ae^{m_1 t} + Be^{m_2 t}$ for heavy damping, when $k^2 - 4\omega^2 > 0$

$x = (A + Bt)e^{-\frac{k}{2}t}$ for critical damping, when $k^2 - 4\omega^2 = 0$

$x = e^{-\frac{k}{2}t}\left(C \sin \frac{\alpha}{2} t + D \cos \frac{\alpha}{2} t\right)$ for light damping,

when $k^2 - 4\omega^2 < 0$ and where $\alpha^2 = 4\omega^2 - k^2$.

4 The general solution of the differential equation p 58

$$\frac{d^2x}{dt^2} + k\frac{dx}{dt} + \omega^2 x = f(t)$$

is made up of two parts, namely,

$$x = x_c(t) + x_p(t)$$

where $x_c(t)$ is the general solution of the associated homogeneous equation (i.e. the right-hand side of the equation is zero) which is

$$\frac{d^2x}{dt^2} + k\frac{dx}{dt} + \omega^2 x = 0$$

and $x_p(t)$ is one particular solution of the full equation.

5 If $f(t)$ is a polynomial of degree n, then the particular solution will also be a polynomial of degree n. For example, if $f(t)$ is of the form $3t^2 + 7t + 5$ then the particular solution will be of the form $at^2 + bt + c$. p 58

6 If $f(x)$ is an exponential function, e.g., $5e^{-7t}$, then the particular solution is of the same form, i.e., Ce^{-7t}. p 60

7 If $f(x)$ is a trigonometric function such as $3 \sin \omega t$, then the particular solution will be of the form $C \sin \omega t + D \cos \omega t$. p 60

8 If a system is allowed to oscillate freely, it will do so at what is called its natural frequency. If the forcing function has the same frequency as the natural frequency, then resonance takes place. p 66

Test yourself — What to review

1 A block, B, of mass 5 kg, is attached to one end of a spring. The other end of the spring is fixed at A. The spring and block rest on a smooth horizontal table, as shown in the diagram. A resistive force of magnitude $25v$ N acts on the particle when it has speed v. The spring has natural length a m and modulus of elasticity $20a$ N. The block is set into motion with a velocity of $2\ \text{m s}^{-1}$ at a distance a m from A. — *Section 3.1*

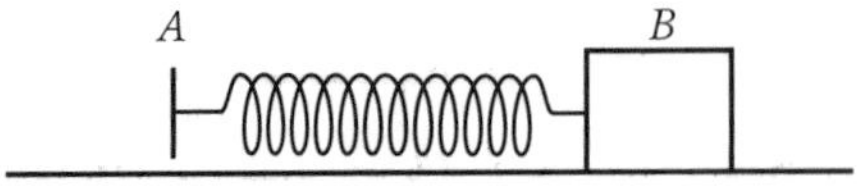

(a) Show that

$$\frac{d^2x}{dt^2} + 5\frac{dx}{dt} + 4x = 0$$

where x is the displacement of the block from its initial position at time t s.

(b) Find the solution of this differential equation.

---

2 A particle oscillates, subject to a resistive force and a forcing force. The motion is such that — *Section 3.2*

$$\frac{d^2x}{dt^2} + 2\frac{dx}{dt} + 5x = \cos 3t$$

where x is the displacement of the particle from its equilibrium position at time t s.

(a) Find the general solution of this differential equation.

(b) If the particle is released from rest at a distance of 0.2 m from its equilibrium position, find x at time t.

---

3 A spring-mass system consists of a block, of mass 2 kg, fixed to a spring on a smooth horizontal surface. The motion is not damped in any way. The spring has modulus of elasticity 40 N and natural length 0.2 m. A forcing function $f(t) = \cos(pt)$ is applied to the block. The block starts at rest at its equilibrium position. — *Section 3.2*

Find expressions for the position of the block at time t if:

(a) $p = 8$, **(b)** $p = 10$.

Test yourself ANSWERS

1 (b) $x = \frac{2}{3}(e^{-4t} - e^{t})$.

2 (a) $x = e^{-t}(A\cos 2t + B\sin 2t) - \frac{1}{13}\cos 3t + \frac{3}{26}\sin 3t$;

(b) $x = e^{-t}\left(\frac{18}{65}\cos 2t - \frac{9}{260}\sin 2t\right) - \frac{1}{13}\cos 3t + \frac{3}{26}\sin 3t$.

3 (a) $x = -\frac{1}{72}\cos 10t + \frac{1}{72}\cos 8t$;

(b) $x = \frac{t}{40}\sin 10t$.

CHAPTER 4

Impulsive motion

Learning objectives

After studying this chapter you should be able to:

- find the impulse of a variable force
- find the impulse in an inextensible string.

4.1 Introduction

In many previous considerations of impulse there has been a sudden change in momentum of a particle, for example, when two snooker balls collide, or when a cricket ball is struck. The forces, which cause these sudden changes in momentum, have not usually been considered. However, the relationship between force and change in momentum has been discussed. In the first section of this chapter we investigate the forces, which act over a small period in time, that cause these seemingly sudden changes in momentum. These forces can vary considerably in magnitude and it is necessary, first of all, to define exactly what we mean by the impulse of a variable force.

4.2 Impulse of a variable force

When a constant force, $\mathbf{F}$ (in newtons), acts on a particle, of mass m kg, for t s, the impulse of the force has been defined by

$$\mathbf{I} = \mathbf{F}t.$$

If $\mathbf{F}$ is the resultant force on the particle, then it has been shown that

$$\mathbf{I} = m\mathbf{v} - m\mathbf{u}$$

where $\mathbf{u}$ and $\mathbf{v}$ are the initial and final velocities of the particle during the interval of t s.

That is, the **impulse** of the **resultant force** on a particle is equal to the change in momentum of the particle.

There are many instances where the force $\mathbf{F}$ is not constant, and so a more general approach is required. Suppose a force $\mathbf{F} = \mathbf{F}(t)$ (in newtons) acts on a particle of mass m kg, for the time interval $t = t_1$ to $t = t_2$.

The impulse of a variable force **F** is defined by

$$\mathbf{I} = \int_{t_1}^{t_2} \mathbf{F}\,\mathrm{d}t$$

If **F** is the resultant force on the particle (whose mass is assumed constant), then the impulse of **F** is given by,

$$\mathbf{I} = \int_{t_1}^{t_2} \mathbf{F}\,\mathrm{d}t = m\int_{t_1}^{t_2} \mathbf{a}\,\mathrm{d}t = m[\mathbf{v}]_{t_1}^{t_2} = m\mathbf{v} - m\mathbf{u}$$

$$\mathbf{I} = m\mathbf{v} - m\mathbf{u}$$

This shows that the new definition is consistent with the case when **F** is constant.

Worked example 4.1

A force **F** N, defined by,

$$\mathbf{F} = \begin{cases} 2t\mathbf{i} & 0 \leqslant t < 4 \\ 2(8-t)\mathbf{i} & 4 \leqslant t \leqslant 8 \end{cases}$$

acts on a particle of mass $\frac{1}{2}$ kg, between $t = 0$ and $t = 8$. The particle starts from rest. Find the velocity of the particle when $t = 8$.

Solution

First find the impulse on the particle.

$$\int_0^8 \mathbf{F}\,\mathrm{d}t = \left[t^2\mathbf{i}\right]_0^4 + \left[(16t - t^2)\mathbf{i}\right]_4^8$$

$$= 16\mathbf{i} + 64\mathbf{i} - 48\mathbf{i} = 32\mathbf{i}$$

Now use the fact that the impulse is equal to the change in the momentum.

$$\tfrac{1}{2}\mathbf{v} = 32\mathbf{i} \Rightarrow \mathbf{v} = 64\mathbf{i}$$

Worked example 4.2

A snooker ball, of mass m, hits a side cushion on a snooker table, at right angles to the cushion, with speed u. The coefficient of restitution between the ball and the cushion is e. The ball is in contact with the cushion for $2T$ s. Two famous snooker players John and Steven suggest different models for the force of the cushion on the snooker ball.

(a) John suggests that this force increases uniformly to a maximum of P N, (when $t = T$), after which time it decreases uniformly, according to

$$F(t) = \begin{cases} \dfrac{P}{T}t & 0 \leqslant t < T \\ \dfrac{P}{T}(2T - t) & T \leqslant t \leqslant 2T \end{cases}$$

(b) Steven prefers a quadratic model where the maximum force is Q N (again when $t = T$) according to

$$F(t) = Q - \frac{Q}{T^2}(t - T)^2$$

Find the values of P and Q in each of the two models, in terms of m, u, e and T.

Solution

(a) The graph of John's force is as shown in the diagram.

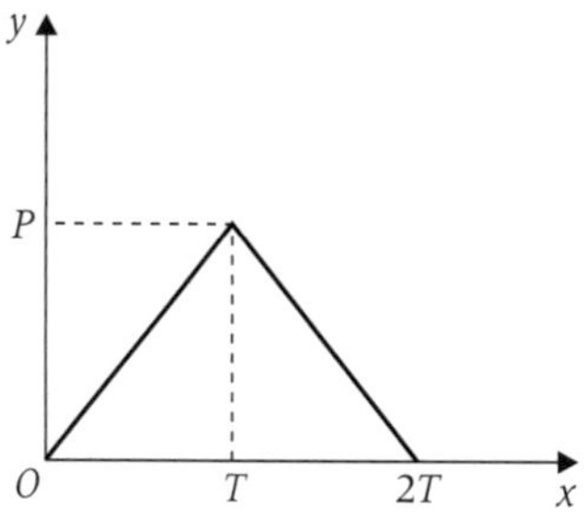

The impulse of John's force is by definition $\int_0^{2T} F\,dt$, which is just the area under the graph of $F(t)$. So in this case the impulse of $F(t)$ is simply the area of the triangle.

Hence, the area under the graph is equal to the change in momentum of the ball.

$$\tfrac{1}{2} \times 2T \times P = meu + mu$$

$$P = \frac{mu(1 + e)}{T}$$

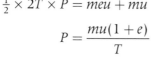

(b) The graph of Steven's force is shown in the diagram.

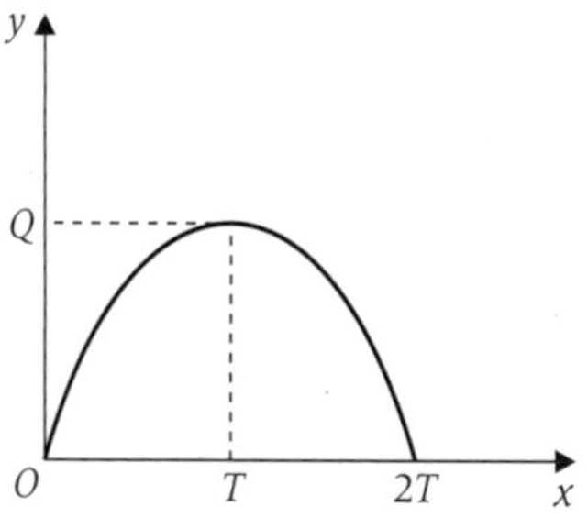

The impulse of Steven's force must be found by integration.

$$\mathbf{I} = \int_0^{2T} Q - \frac{Q}{T^2}(t - T)^2\,dt = \frac{4TQ}{3}$$

Considering the change in momentum of the ball gives,

$$\frac{4TQ}{3} = mu(1 + e).$$

Hence,

$$Q = \frac{3mu(1 + e)}{4T}.$$

Worked example 4.3

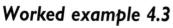

A ball falls vertically and bounces on the horizontal ground. The speed of the ball before impact is u m s^{-1} and its speed after impact is $\frac{u}{2}$ m s^{-1}. The ball is in contact with the floor for $\frac{1}{2}$ s. The force of the floor on the ball is modelled by

$$F = k \sin 2\pi t \qquad 0 \leqslant t \leqslant \tfrac{1}{2}$$

(a) Find the impulse of F.

(b) Find k in terms of u and g.

Solution

(a) The impulse of F is

$$\int_0^{\frac{1}{2}} F\,\mathrm{d}t = \left[-\frac{k}{2\pi}\cos 2\pi t\right]_0^{\frac{1}{2}} = \frac{k}{\pi}.$$

(b) The resultant force on the particle is given by $F - mg$. The impulse of this force (**not just the impulse of F**) equals the change in momentum of the ball.

Hence,

$$\int_0^{\frac{1}{2}} (F - mg)\,\mathrm{d}t = m\frac{u}{2} + mu = \frac{3mu}{2}$$

$$\therefore \quad \frac{k}{\pi} - \frac{mg}{2} = \frac{3mu}{2}$$

$$\Rightarrow \quad k = \frac{1}{2}\pi m(3u + g)$$

EXERCISE 4A

1 A snooker ball, of mass 200 g, hits a side cushion on a snooker table, at right angles to the cushion, with speed $1\,\mathrm{m\,s^{-1}}$, and rebounds with speed $0.8\,\mathrm{m\,s^{-1}}$. The ball remains in contact with the cushion for one tenth of a second. The force of the cushion on the ball during contact is modelled by the function $F(t)$, defined below. Find the maximum value of this force.

$$F(t) = \begin{cases} kt & 0 \leqslant t < 0.05 \\ k(0.1 - t) & 0.05 \leqslant t \leqslant 0.1 \end{cases}$$

2 A ball, of mass 20 g, is dropped and hits a horizontal surface at $5\,\mathrm{m\,s^{-1}}$ and rebounds with a speed of $3\,\mathrm{m\,s^{-1}}$. The force, in newtons, of the ground on the ball is modelled by

$$F(t) = \begin{cases} kt & 0 \leqslant t < 0.1 \\ k(0.2 - t) & 0.1 \leqslant t \leqslant 0.2 \end{cases}$$

where t is measured in seconds and k is a constant.

(a) Sketch the graph of F against t.

(b) Find k.

3 In each of the following cases find the impulse of the given force over the stated time interval.

(a) $\mathbf{F} = 3t^2\mathbf{i} + 2t\mathbf{j} + \mathbf{k} \qquad 1 \leqslant t \leqslant 3$

(b) $\mathbf{F} = \cos t\,\mathbf{i} + \sin t\,\mathbf{j} \qquad 0 \leqslant t \leqslant 2\pi$

(c) $\mathbf{F} = \ln(4 - t)\mathbf{i} \qquad 1 \leqslant t \leqslant 3$

4 A ball, of mass m, is dropped and hits the horizontal ground with speed $u\,\mathrm{m\,s^{-1}}$. It rebounds with speed $\frac{1}{2}u\,\mathrm{m\,s^{-1}}$, and is in contact with the floor for $2T$ s. The force of the ground on the ball is modelled by

$$F(t) = at^2 + bt + c \qquad 0 \leqslant t \leqslant 2T$$

such that $F(0) = 0$ and $F(2T) = 0$ and where a, b and c are constants.

(a) Sketch the graph of F against t.

(b) Find the constants a, b and c in terms of m, u, g and T.

(c) What is the maximum value of F?

5

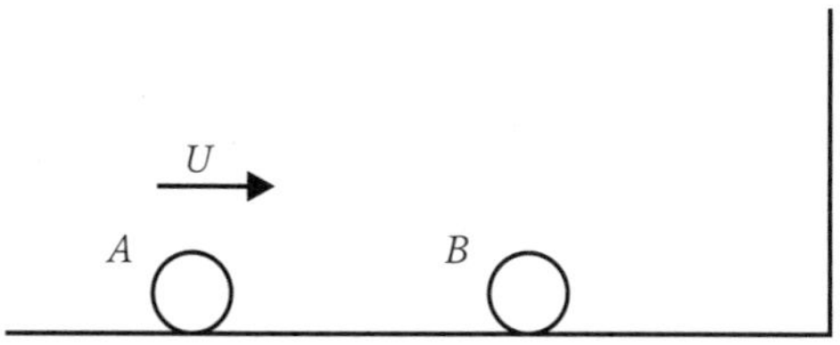

A smooth sphere, A, moves in a straight line across a smooth horizontal surface with speed U, directly towards a stationary smooth sphere, B, as shown in the diagram. Subsequently A and B collide. The spheres are of equal radius and their masses are $3m$ and m respectively.

(a) Assuming that the collision between the spheres is perfectly elastic, show that after the collision the sphere B has speed $\frac{3}{2}U$.

(b) The sphere B subsequently collides with a wall, which is perpendicular to its direction of motion. The coefficient of restitution between the sphere B and the wall is e. Given that after B rebounds from the wall, both spheres are moving with the same speed, find the value of e.

(c) The diagram shows a very simple model of the way the magnitude of the force, F, between the sphere B and the wall varies while the sphere is in contact with the wall. The greatest value of the magnitude of this force is $2000mU$.

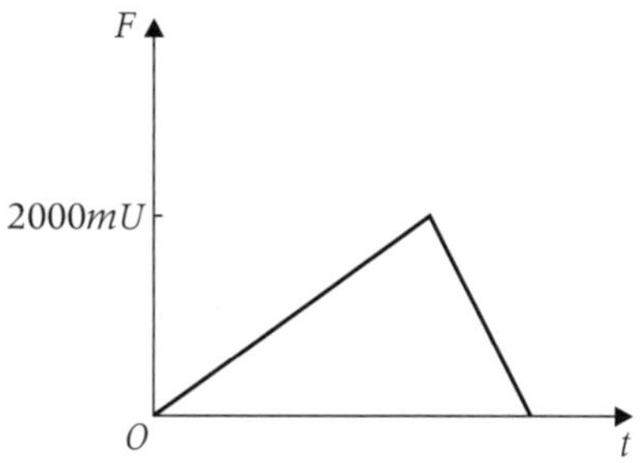

(i) Use this model to estimate the total time the sphere B is in contact with the wall.

(ii) State one criticism of this model of the magnitude of this force.

6 An athlete, of mass m kg, is bouncing vertically on a trampoline. When the athlete is in contact with the trampoline the magnitude of the force of the trampoline on the athlete is modelled by $f(t)$, defined by

$$f(t) = a \sin \pi t \qquad 0 \leqslant t \leqslant 1.$$

In a particular manoeuvre the athlete hits the trampoline with speed u and leaves the trampoline with speed $\frac{3}{2}u$.

(a) Find the change in momentum of the athlete in terms of u and m.

(b) Find the impulse of the trampoline on the athlete in terms of u, m and g.

(c) Find a in terms of u, m and g.

7 A skydiver, of mass 90 kg, free-falls and reaches a vertical speed of $60\,\text{m s}^{-1}$ when his parachute is opened. The parachute reduces the speed of the skydiver to $3\,\text{m s}^{-1}$ in 2 s. The upwards force of the parachute on the skydiver is modelled by $f(t)$, as described by the graph below.

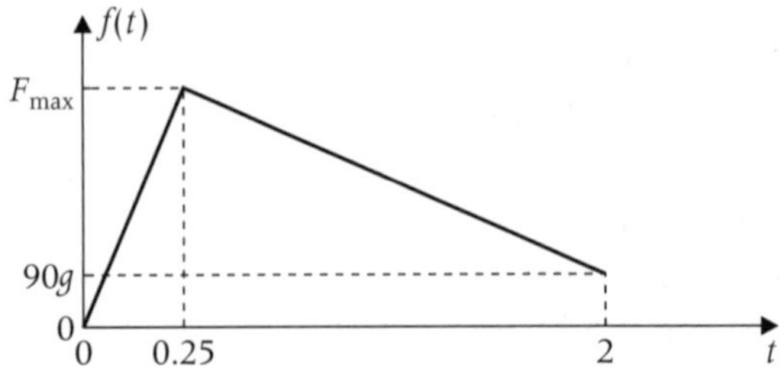

(a) Find the resultant impulse on the skydiver.

(b) Find the impulse of $f(t)$ on the skydiver.

(c) Find the maximum force that the parachute exerts on the skydiver.

8 A beach ball, of mass 50 g, falls vertically and hits the ground with speed $0.5\,\text{m s}^{-1}$. The force of the ground on the ball during contact is modelled by the function $f(t)$ defined by

$$f(t) = a(2 + \sin 2\pi t) \qquad 0 \leqslant t \leqslant \tfrac{1}{2}.$$

The ball rebounds with speed $0.25\,\text{m s}^{-1}$.

(a) Find the impulse of $f(t)$ on the ball, in terms of a.

(b) Find the impulse of gravity on the ball.

(c) Find a.

9 A car, of mass 1 tonne, travels on a horizontal road and crashes straight into a wall at a speed of $10\,\text{m s}^{-1}$. The force of the wall on the car is modelled by $f(t)$, as described by the graph.

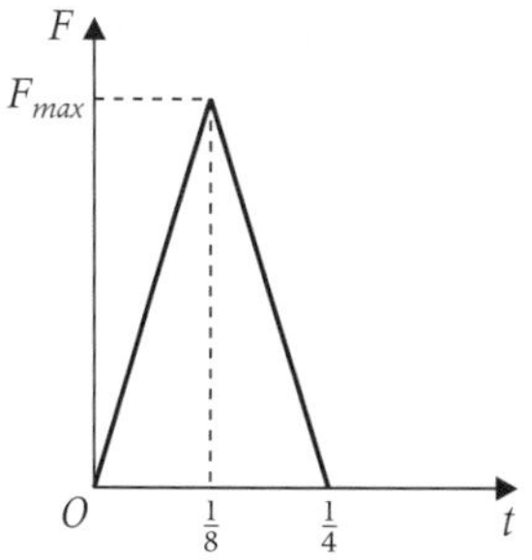

(a) Assuming that the engine and the brakes are unable to exert any force on the car during the collision, find the maximum value of $f(t)$, $F_{\max}$, if the car is brought to rest by the wall.

In order to reduce the maximum force on the car in such collisions, the designers incorporate a crumple zone into the vehicle, which increases the time to bring the car to rest. The force of the wall on the car (with the crumple zone), $g(t)$, under the same collision as described above, is defined by

$$g(t) = G_{\max} - \frac{1}{10}\left(t - \tfrac{1}{4}\right)^2 \qquad 0 \leqslant t \leqslant \tfrac{1}{2}.$$

(b) Find the maximum value of the force of the wall on the car, $G_{\max}$, during the collision.

4

4.3 Impulsive tension

Suppose a particle, P, is connected to one end of a light inextensible string. When the string is taut the tension acts on P. If the tension acts over a period of time then the particle receives an impulse. Sometimes, however, the string may suddenly tighten (so a large tension force acts over a small period of time) and so similarly the particle receives an impulse and consequently its momentum is changed. In these cases we neglect the time interval over which the impulse acts and treat it as an instantaneous impulse. Such an impulse in an inextensible string is called an impulsive tension, which will, of course, be parallel to the string.

> When an impulsive tension acts on a particle its momentum changes, but only in the direction of the string. If the particle is initially stationary then it will begin to move in the direction of the impulse, i.e., in the direction of the string.

If the string connects two particles, then it is important to note the following principles:

- Each particle receives an impulse equal in magnitude, but opposite in direction.
- The impulse–momentum principle must be applied separately to each particle involved.

Worked example 4.4

Two particles, P and Q, each of mass m kg, lie at rest on a smooth horizontal table, a distance a apart. The particles are connected, one at each end, to a light inextensible string, of length $2a$, which is initially slack. Particle Q is projected horizontally with speed $2u$, in the direction perpendicular to the initial line PQ. Find, in terms of u, the speeds of P and Q immediately after the string tightens.

Solution

The diagram shows the velocities of the particles just before and just after collision. The impulses in the string, which cause the change in the particles' momentum, are shown in the before diagram.

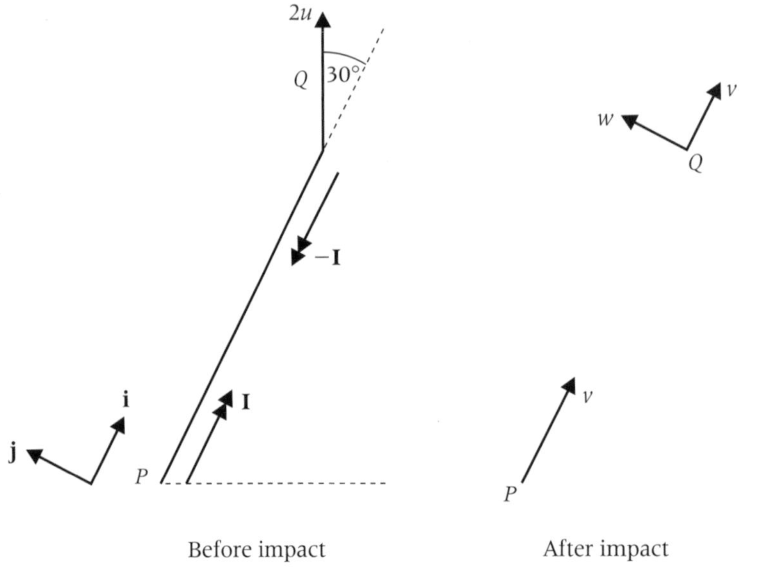

Let **i** and **j** be unit vectors parallel and perpendicular to the string at the point of impact, as shown.

Applying the impulse–momentum principle to particles P and Q separately, we get

$$\mathbf{I} = mv\mathbf{i} \qquad [1]$$

$$-\mathbf{I} = m(v\mathbf{i} + w\mathbf{j}) - m(2u\cos 30^\circ\mathbf{i} + 2u\sin 30^\circ\mathbf{j})$$

$$\mathbf{I} = m(\sqrt{3}u - v)\mathbf{i} + m(u - w)\mathbf{j} \qquad [2]$$

Equating the two expressions for **I** gives

$$\sqrt{3}u - v = v$$

$$v = \frac{\sqrt{3}}{2}u$$

and $u = w$.

After impact the string remains taut and so the components of the velocities of the particles parallel to the string will be equal (v). This happens because the string is inextensible. In reality **all** strings are **elastic** and so the components of the velocity parallel to the string would not be equal.

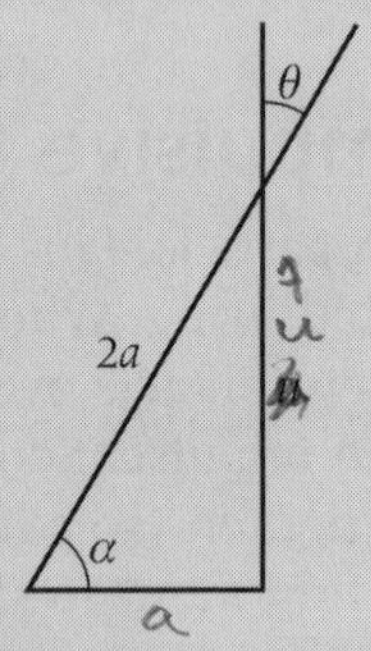

$\cos\alpha = \frac{1}{2}$

$\therefore\ \alpha = 60^\circ$

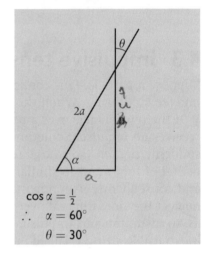

$\theta = 30^\circ$

The speed of P is therefore $\frac{\sqrt{3}}{2}u$, and the speed of Q is $\sqrt{\frac{3}{4}u^2 + u^2} = \frac{\sqrt{7}}{2}u$.

Worked example 4.5

Two particles, P and Q, of mass 2 kg and 5 kg, respectively, are attached to the ends of a light inextensible string, which passes over a smooth fixed pulley. The system is released from rest with both parts of the string taut and vertical. When P is travelling with speed u it hits and coalesces with a stationary particle of mass 1 kg. Find the speeds of the particles after the collision, the impulsive tension in the string, and the impulse of the string on the pulley.

Solution

The diagram shows the velocities of the particles just before and just after collision. The impulses in the string, which cause the change in the particles' momentum, are shown in the 'before' diagram.

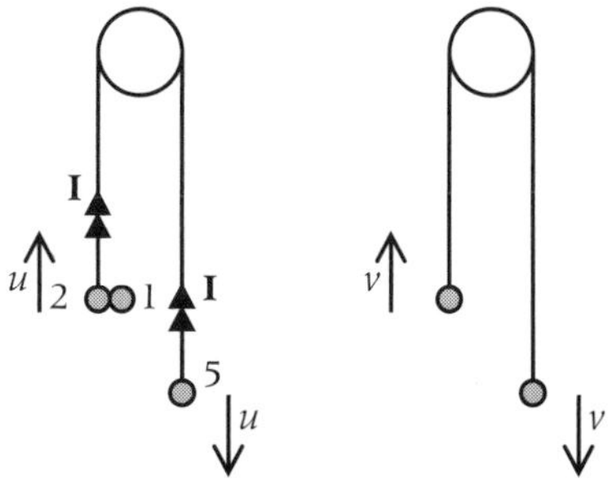

Before impact After impact

Applying the impulse–momentum principle to P and Q separately we get

$$I = 3v - 2u$$
$$I = 5u - 5v$$

These equations are simultaneous equations for I and v in terms of u. Subtracting them gives

$$v = \frac{7}{8}u, \quad \text{and} \quad I = \frac{5}{8}u.$$

When the particles are in motion the force on the pulley will equal $2T$ downwards, where T is the tension in the string, as shown in the diagram.

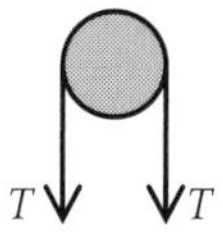

When the particles collide the impulse of the string on the pulley will equal $2I$ downwards, where I is the impulsive tension in the string, as shown in the diagram.

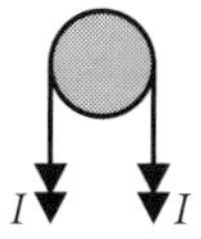

The impulse on the pulley will therefore be $\frac{5}{4}u$.

EXERCISE 4B

1 Two particles, P and Q, of mass m kg and $2m$ kg, respectively, lie at rest on a smooth horizontal table, a distance a apart. The particles are connected, one at each end, to a light inextensible string, of length $2a$, which is initially slack. Particle Q is projected horizontally with speed $2u$, in the direction perpendicular to the initial line PQ. Find, in terms of u, the speeds of P and Q immediately after the string tightens.

2 A particle, of mass m kg, is attached to one end of a light inextensible string of length $2a$. The other end of the string is attached to a fixed point O on a smooth horizontal table. The particle is projected horizontally from a point A on the table, where $OA = a$, in a direction perpendicular to OA with speed $2u$. Find the speed of the particle after the string becomes taut, and the impulsive tension in the string.

3 Two particles, P and Q, of mass 2 kg and 5 kg, respectively, are attached to the ends of a light inextensible string, of length $2a$. Initially the particles lie at rest on a smooth horizontal plane, and are a distance $2a$ apart. The particle Q receives a horizontal impulse of magnitude 20 N s. The direction of the impulse is at 60° to the line of PQ produced. Find the speeds of P and Q after the impact and the magnitude of the impulsive tension in the string.

4 Two particles, A and B, of mass $2m$ and $3m$, respectively, are attached to the ends of a light inextensible string of length c and are placed close together on a horizontal table. The particle A is projected vertically upwards with speed $\sqrt{6gc}$.

(a) Show that at the instant immediately after the string tightens, B is moving with velocity $\frac{4}{3}\sqrt{gc}$.

(b) State the impulse of the tension in the string.

(c) Find the height to which A rises above the table before it comes to instantaneous rest.

(d) Calculate the loss in kinetic energy due to the tightening of the string. [A]

5 A particle P, of mass $2m$, is connected to a particle Q, of mass $3m$, by means of a light string, which passes over a small smooth pulley. The particles are released from rest with the string taut and its hanging parts vertical.

(a) Calculate the acceleration of P and the tension in the string.

At the instant when P is moving with velocity v it collides and coalesces with a stationary particle, of mass $3m$, to form a particle P_1.

(b) Prove that the velocity of P_1 immediately after the collision is $\frac{5v}{8}$.

(c) Calculate the magnitude of the impulse of the tension in the string.

(d) Calculate the loss in kinetic energy of the whole system due to the collision.

The string breaks and particle Q hits a horizontal floor when moving with speed u and bounces to a height $\frac{u^2}{6g}$ above the floor.

(e) Calculate the coefficient of restitution between Q and the floor. [A]

6 Two particles, of mass $4m$ and $3m$, respectively, are at each end of a light inextensible string which passes over a smooth fixed pulley. The particles move in a vertical plane with both the hanging parts of the string vertical. Write down the equation of motion for each of the particles and hence determine, in terms of m and/or g as appropriate, the magnitude of the acceleration of the particles and of the tension in the string.

When the particle of mass $3m$ is moving upwards with a speed V it picks up from rest at a point A an additional mass, $2m$, so as to form a composite Q of mass $5m$. Determine:

(a) the initial speed of the system,

(b) the impulsive tension in the string immediately the additional particle has been picked up,

(c) the height above A to which Q rises. [A]

7 (a) Two particles, A and B, of mass $3m$ and $5m$, respectively, are placed on a smooth horizontal table. The particle A is projected along the table with speed u directly towards B, which is at rest. After the impact A continues to move in the same direction but with speed $\frac{u}{6}$. Find:

(i) the speed of B after impact,

(ii) the coefficient of restitution between A and B,

(iii) the loss in kinetic energy due to the collision.

(b) The same particles, A and B, are now connected by a light inextensible string and are placed side by side on a smooth horizontal table. The particle A is projected horizontally, directly away from B, with a speed v. Calculate:

(i) the resulting common speed of the two particles after the string has tightened,
(ii) the magnitude of the impulse in the string when the string tightens,
(iii) the loss in kinetic energy due to the tightening of the string. [A]

8 Two particles, A and B, of mass m and M, respectively, are connected by a light inextensible string of length $3a$. Initially A is held at rest alongside a small smooth pulley, which is fixed at a height $2a$ above a horizontal table. The string is slack and passes over the pulley, which is vertically above the particle B on the table. The particle A is now released. Show that when B is jerked into motion both particles begin to move with speed u, where

$$u = \frac{m\sqrt{2ga}}{M + m}.$$

[You should assume that the taut strings on each side of the pulley are vertical and the length of string in contact with the pulley is negligible.]

Find in terms of m, M and g, the tension in the string whilst both particles are moving.

Determine the value of $\frac{m}{M}$, which is such that when A is first instantaneously at rest, it has just reached the table.

For this value of $\frac{m}{M}$, briefly describe the next stage of the motion of the system up to the instant at which one of the particles comes to instantaneous rest. [A]

9 The figure shows a particle, A, of mass $10m$, on a smooth plane inclined at an angle θ to the horizontal, where $\sin\theta = 0.6$. The particle is attached to one end of a light inextensible string, which passes over a smooth fixed pulley, P, at the highest point of the plane. A particle, B, of mass $10m$, is attached to the other end of the string parallel to the line of greatest slope of the plane but not in contact with the plane and BP vertical, with B being at a distance d above an inelastic horizontal floor.

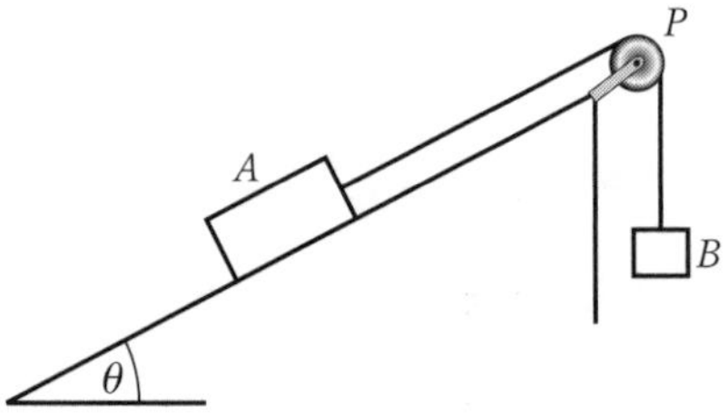

The system is released from rest so that B starts to fall. Find the acceleration of B and the tension in the string.

Determine:

(a) the further distance that A moves up the plane after B has struck the floor, (you may assume that A does not reach the pulley),

(b) the time that B remains in contact with the floor,

(c) the speed with which B is jerked off the floor. [A]

10 Three particles, A, B and C, of mass m, $2m$ and $4m$, respectively, are joined, with the strings taut, by two light inextensible strings, AB and BC. The particles are initially at rest in a straight line on a smooth horizontal plane. An impulse of magnitude J is then applied to A in the sense from B to A. Find the initial speed of A.

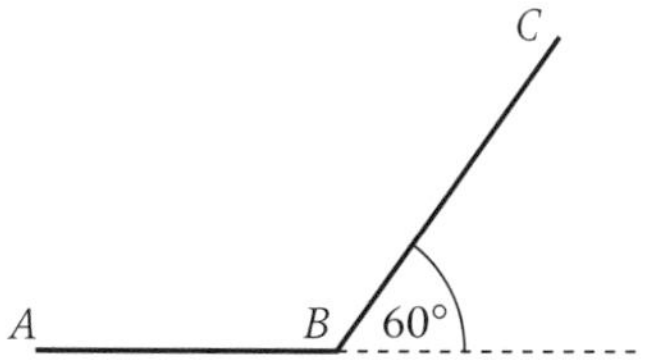

The particles are arranged as shown in the figure and placed at rest on a smooth horizontal plane with the strings taut and with the angle between BC and AB equal to $60°$.

An impulse of magnitude J is again applied to A in the sense from B to A. Show that the initial speed of A is five times that of C and find the initial speed of A in terms of J and m. (Hint: the component of the initial velocity of B in the direction CB is equal to the speed of C.)
Find also, in terms of J, the magnitude of the impulse in AB. [A]

Key point summary

1 The impulse of a variable force $\mathbf{F}$ is defined by p 76

$$\mathbf{I} = \int_{t_1}^{t_2} \mathbf{F}\,\mathrm{d}t$$

2 When an impulsive tension acts on a particle its momentum changes, but only in the direction of the string. If the particle is initially stationary then it will begin to move in the direction of the impulse, i.e., in the direction of the string. p 81

Test yourself

What to review

1 The graph shows the resultant force acting on a ball, of mass 200 g, as it bounces on a horizontal surface. The ball rebounds vertically at $4\,\text{m s}^{-1}$. *Section 4.2*

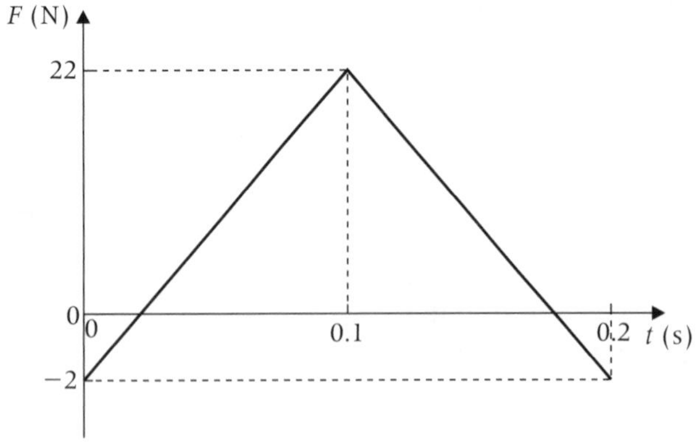

(a) Find the impulse on the ball.

(b) Find the speed at which the ball hits the surface.

---

2 Two particles, of mass 0.2 kg and 0.4 kg, are attached to the ends of a light inextensible string passing over a smooth fixed pulley. The particles are released from rest with both sides of the string taut and vertical. At the instant when the particles have a common speed of $2\,\text{m s}^{-1}$ the heavier particle hits a horizontal surface from which it does not rebound (the surface is referred to as inelastic). *Section 4.3*

(a) Find the speed with which the heavier particle is first jerked into motion, and the impulsive tension in the string.

(b) When the same particles are moving with a speed of $2\,\text{m s}^{-1}$ (the heavier one downwards again) the lighter particle picks up a stationary particle of mass 0.5 kg, which coalesces with the lighter particle after the collision. Find the common speed of the particles immediately after the collision, and find the impulse of the string on the pulley.

Test yourself ANSWERS

1 **(a)** 2 N s; **(b)** $6\,\text{m s}^{-1}$.

2 **(a)** $\frac{2}{3}\,\text{m s}^{-1}$, $\frac{4}{15}$ N s; **(b)** $1.09\,\text{m s}^{-1}$, 0.727 N s.

Motion with variable mass

Learning objectives

After studying this chapter you should be able to:

- apply the impulse–momentum principle to a body, which either loses or gains mass, to derive an equation of motion
- find the velocity, mass or displacement of a rocket as a function of time
- find the velocity, mass or displacement of a raindrop as a function of time.

5.1 Introduction

Newton's second law states that the resultant force on a particle is proportional to the rate of change of its **momentum**. In problems previously encountered, the mass of the particle has remained constant, and so the equation

$$\mathbf{F} = m\frac{\mathrm{d}\mathbf{v}}{\mathrm{d}t}$$

has been used to arrive at an equation of motion. However, in this chapter we investigate the problem where the mass cannot be assumed to be constant. There are two main applications: a rocket leaving the earth's surface to travel into space; and a falling raindrop, which increases its mass as it falls.

In these applications, we must use the more general statement of Newton's second law,

$$\mathbf{F} = \frac{\mathrm{d}(m\mathbf{v})}{\mathrm{d}t}.$$

In fact, we will use a small interval of time, δt, for which,

$$\mathbf{F} \approx \frac{\delta(m\mathbf{v})}{\delta t}$$

$$\mathbf{F}\delta t = \delta(m\mathbf{v})$$

$\mathbf{F}\delta t =$ change in momentum in time δt

This result is known as the impulse–momentum principle, which states that **the impulse of the resultant force on a particle is equal to the change of its linear momentum**.

We will consider the two cases of loss or gain in mass separately, but in each case an equation of motion will be found from first principles. This is a more reliable approach than applying formulae.

5.2 Problems involving decreasing mass

Worked example 5.1

A rocket launches from the surface of the earth and rises vertically. The rocket powers itself by ejecting burned fuel at a constant rate, backwards, at a constant speed, U, relative to the rocket. Its engines burn fuel at a constant rate so that the mass of the rocket, at time t, is given by $m = M_0 + M_1(1 - kt)$, where M_0 is the mass of the rocket and M_1 is the mass of the initial load of fuel. Assuming that the acceleration due to gravity is constant show that the equation of motion of the rocket is given by

$$-mg = m\frac{dv}{dt} + U\frac{dm}{dt}.$$

Solve the equation and find the velocity of the rocket when all of its fuel has been burned.

Solution

Let the velocity of the rocket at time t s after launch be v. Consider a small time interval $(t, t + \delta t)$. The following diagram shows the ejection of a small amount of fuel, during the time interval.

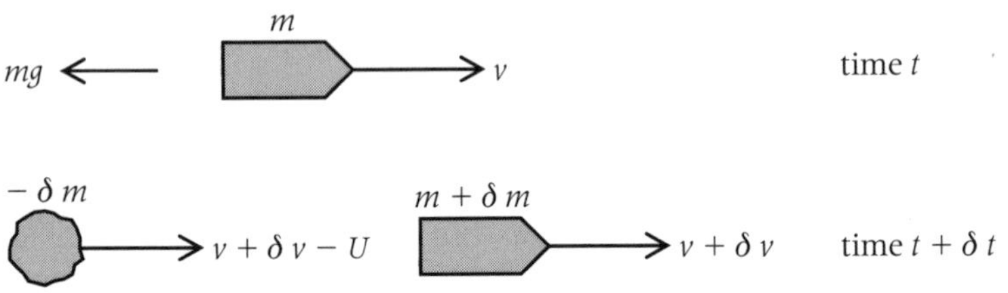

Note that the mass of the rocket and its remaining fuel at the end of the time interval is $m + \delta m$. This means that δm will be negative. This is so that the rate of change of the mass of the rocket will be represented by $\frac{dm}{dt}$, which of course, is negative.

Applying the impulse–momentum principle,

$$-mg\delta t = (m + \delta m)(v + \delta v) + (-\delta m)(v + \delta v - U) - mv$$

$$-mg\delta t = m\delta v + U\delta m$$

Dividing by δt and letting $\delta t \to 0$ gives

$$-mg = m\frac{dv}{dt} + U\frac{dm}{dt}$$

Note that if the rocket is travelling through space then no gravitational force acts, then the impulse–momentum equation reduces to

$$m\delta v + U\delta m = 0.$$

This can be integrated by dividing by δm which gives

$$\frac{dv}{dm} = \frac{-U}{m}.$$

Dividing by m gives $-g = \frac{dv}{dt} + \frac{U}{m}\frac{dm}{dt} = \frac{dv}{dt} + U\frac{d(\ln m)}{dt}$.

Hence,

$$C - gt = v + U \ln m.$$

When $t = 0$, $v = 0$, and $m = M_0 + M_1$

$$C = U \ln (M_0 + M_1)$$

$$v = U \ln\left(\frac{M_0 + M_1}{M_0 + M_1(1 - kt)}\right) - gt$$

When all the fuel is spent $t = \frac{1}{k}$, so the final speed of the rocket is given by

$$v = U \ln\left(1 + \frac{M_1}{M_0}\right) - \frac{g}{k}.$$

Worked example 5.2

Bill, a builder, of mass 100 kg, stands on a platform, of mass 50 kg, which is held off the ground by a light cable. The cable passes over a smooth pulley and is attached to a bag of sand, of mass 150 kg. Initially the builder, platform and sand hang freely in equilibrium, as shown.

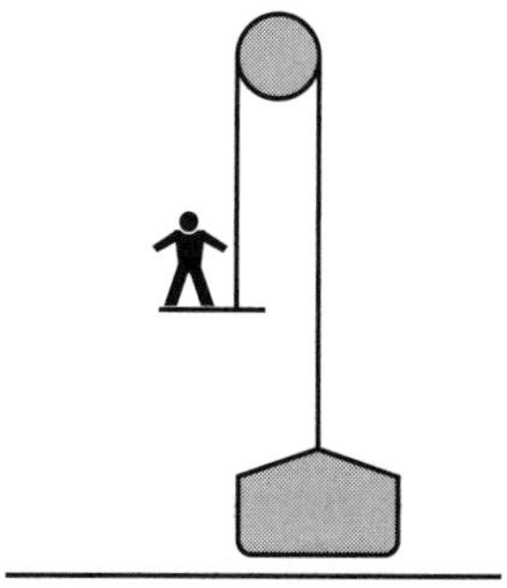

The bag, however, is worn and sand begins to leak at the rate of 1 kg s^{-1}. Find the velocity of the platform t s after the start of the leak, assuming that the bag has not hit the pulley and before the platform reaches the floor.

Solution

The mass of the man and platform remain constant. So if T is the tension in the cable, and v the velocity of the platform, Newton's second law gives

$$150g - T = 150\frac{dv}{dt}. \qquad [1]$$

The bag of sand does not remain constant, however. We must apply the impulse–momentum principle. Let m be the mass of the bag and sand, at time t.

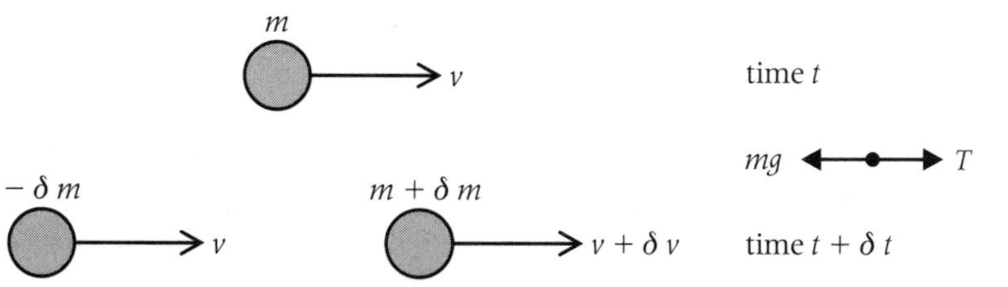

$$(T - mg)\,\delta t = (m + \delta m)(v + \delta v) - \delta m v - mv = m\delta v + \delta m \delta v$$

Ignoring the $\delta m \delta v$ term, dividing by δt, and letting $\delta t \to 0$, gives

$$T - mg = m\frac{\mathrm{d}v}{\mathrm{d}t}. \qquad [2]$$

Adding equations [1] and [2] gives

$$150g - mg = (150 + m)\frac{\mathrm{d}v}{\mathrm{d}t}. \qquad [3]$$

If 1 kg of sand leaks out of the bag per second, then

$$\frac{\mathrm{d}m}{\mathrm{d}t} = -1.$$

Assuming the bag to be light compared to the sand, then

$$m = 150 - t.$$

Equation [3] simplifies to

$$\frac{\mathrm{d}v}{\mathrm{d}t} = \frac{gt}{300 - t} = -g + \frac{300g}{300 - t}$$

$$v = -gt - 300g \ln(300 - t) + c$$

But $v = 0$ when $t = 0$, so $c = 300g \ln 300$, and so

$$v = 300g \ln \frac{300}{300 - t} - gt.$$

EXERCISE 5A

1 A rocket travels through space, such that the only force on it is due to its engines, which eject burned fuel at speed $U\,\mathrm{m\,s^{-1}}$, backwards relative to the motion of the rocket. The rocket is initially moving forwards with speed $V_0\,\mathrm{m\,s^{-1}}$ and has an initial mass (including fuel) of M_0 kg. Find the speed of the rocket after the engines have reduced the mass of the rocket to 90 per cent of its initial mass.

2 A rocket is travelling vertically upwards with speed $v\,\mathrm{m\,s^{-1}}$. Its mass at time t s is $m = M_0 - kt$ (kg). The rocket ejects burned fuel at a constant speed of $U\,\mathrm{m\,s^{-1}}$ relative to the rocket. The rocket is initially at rest. Assuming that the rocket is close to the earth's surface, show that after time t s,

$$\frac{\mathrm{d}v}{\mathrm{d}t} = \frac{kU}{M_0 - kt} - g.$$

Find an expression for the velocity of the rocket at time t.
If half the initial mass of the rocket is fuel find the maximum speed of the rocket.

3 A hot air balloon, of mass M_0 kg, is initially at rest on the ground. A constant lift force of magnitude $M_0 g$ N is maintained using gas burners. Sand begins to leak from the balloon's ballast at a constant rate of $kM_0\,\mathrm{kg\,s^{-1}}$ and so the balloon begins to rise vertically. Assuming that the acceleration due to gravity is constant and neglecting air resistance, find the velocity of the balloon, in terms of g and k, when the mass of the balloon has been reduced by 10 per cent. Find also the height of the balloon at this time.

4 A rocket has an initial mass M_0. It takes off and ejects burned fuel at a constant speed $U\,\mathrm{m\,s^{-1}}$ relative to the rocket such that $\frac{\mathrm{d}m}{\mathrm{d}t} = -kM_0$, where m is the mass of the rocket at time t s after launch. The rocket rises vertically and gravity can be assumed to be constant.

(a) Show that if the rocket is to lift off then $k > \frac{g}{U}$.

(b) Show that the velocity of the rocket at time t is given by

$$v = -U\ln(1 - kt) - gt.$$

(c) Show that the height of the rocket above the launch pad when the mass of the rocket is $\frac{1}{2}M_0$, is given by

$$h = \frac{U}{2k}\left(1 - \ln 2 - \frac{g}{4kU}\right).$$

5 A rocket launches vertically from rest. Its initial mass is M_0 and it ejects burned fuel at a constant speed, U, relative to the rocket. If gravity is assumed constant throughout the motion, show that

$$m\frac{\mathrm{d}v}{\mathrm{d}t} + U\frac{\mathrm{d}m}{\mathrm{d}t} = -mg,$$

where m is the mass of the rocket and v its velocity, at time t s after launch.

Solve the differential equation to find v as a function of t, in each of the following situations, where λ and k are constants.

(a) $\frac{\mathrm{d}m}{\mathrm{d}t} = -kM_0$.

(b) $\frac{\mathrm{d}m}{\mathrm{d}t} = -\lambda \mathrm{e}^{-kt}$.

(c) $\frac{\mathrm{d}m}{\mathrm{d}t} = -km$.

(d) In this case find m as a function of t if $\frac{\mathrm{d}v}{\mathrm{d}t} = k$.

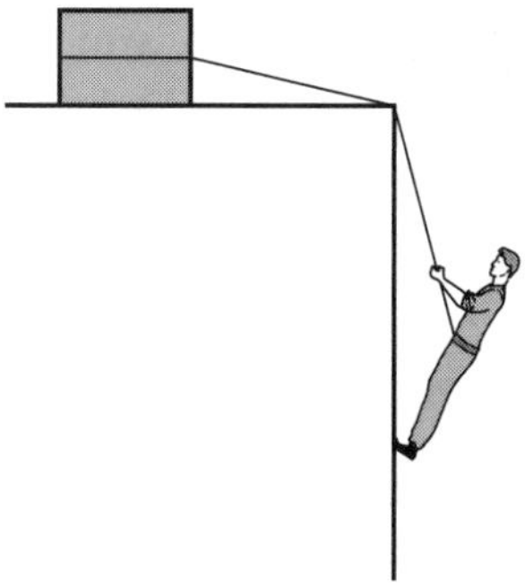

6 Bill, a builder, of mass 100 kg, has been given the job of rendering a high brick wall. After his previous experience with leaking bags of sand he decides to abseil down the wall from the roof of the building concerned. On the roof he notices a large barrel, which says it has mass 2 tonnes. Quite content with this he lassoes the barrel, abseils down, and begins his work, as shown.

Unbeknown to Bill, the barrel contains water and leaks.

(a) If the coefficient of friction between the roof and the barrel is 0.1, at what point does Bill begin to fall? (Neglect any frictional force between the rope and the top of the wall.)

(b) If v is Bill's velocity, at time t s after beginning to fall, and letting $g = 10\,\mathrm{m\,s^{-2}}$, show that

$$\frac{dv}{dt} = \frac{1000 - m}{100 + m},$$

where m is the mass of the barrel at time t.

7 A rocket is launched from the earth's surface and travels vertically upwards. At time t after launch the mass of the rocket is m and it is travelling with velocity v. The exhaust gases are ejected with constant speed c relative to the rocket.

(a) Show that the equation of the motion of the rocket is

$$m\frac{dv}{dt} + c\frac{dm}{dt} = -mg.$$

(b) The initial mass of the rocket is m_0. Ejection of the exhaust gases causes the mass to decrease at a constant rate λ.

(i) Show that in order to achieve lift-off from the ground, the value of c must be greater than $\frac{m_0 g}{\lambda}$.

(ii) Given that c has a value of $\frac{2m_0 g}{\lambda}$ and that the initial mass of the fuel is $\frac{3}{4}m_0$, find in terms of g, the maximum acceleration of the rocket. [A]

5.3 Problems involving increasing mass

In this section we will apply the impulse–momentum principle to situations where the mass of the body involved is increasing.

Worked example 5.3

A small icicle falls from rest through a cloud. The initial mass of the icicle is M_0 kg, and it increases in volume (and mass) at a constant rate of $kM_0\,\mathrm{kg\,s^{-1}}$. Assuming that the acceleration due to gravity is constant throughout the motion, show that the velocity, v, of the icicle t s after its formation is given by

$$\frac{dv}{dt} + \frac{k}{1 + kt}v = g.$$

Find the velocity as a function of time, and the velocity when the mass of the icicle has doubled.

Solution

Let the mass of the icicle at time t be m. We are given $\dfrac{dm}{dt} = kM_0$ and integrating gives $m = M_0(1 + kt)$.

Consider a small time interval $(t, t + \delta t)$.

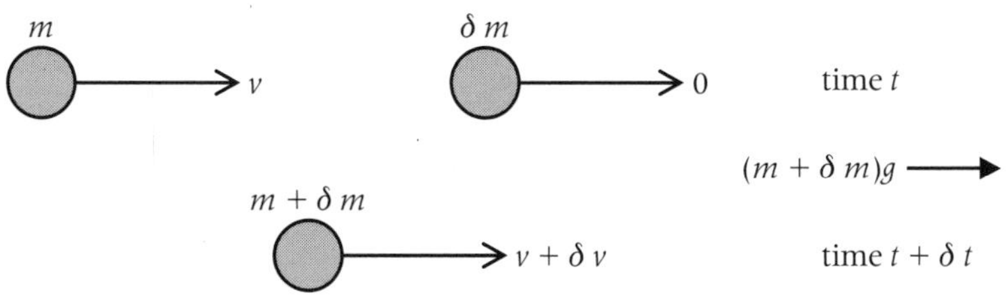

Applying the impulse–momentum principle

$$(m + \delta m)g\delta t = (m + \delta m)(v + \delta v) - mv - \delta m \times 0$$

$$(m + \delta m)g\delta t = m\delta v + v\delta m + \delta v\delta m$$

Dividing by δt, neglecting the $\delta v\delta m$ term, and letting $\delta t \to 0$, gives

$$mg = m\frac{dv}{dt} + v\frac{dm}{dt}.$$

Substituting for $\dfrac{dm}{dt}$ and m gives

$$g = \frac{dv}{dt} + \frac{v}{M_0(1 + kt)} \times kM_0.$$

Hence,

$$\frac{dv}{dt} + \frac{k}{1 + kt}v = g.$$

This is a linear differential equation which can be solved with an integrating factor of $(1 + kt)$. Multiply all the terms of the differential equation by $(1 + kt)$, to give

$$(1 + kt)\frac{dv}{dt} + kv = g(1 + kt).$$

Note that the left-hand side of the equation is the derivative of $(1 + kt)v$.

$$\therefore \quad (1 + kt)v = \int g(1 + kt)\, dt$$

$$(1 + kt)v = \frac{g}{2k}(1 + kt)^2 + C$$

When $t = 0$, $v = 0 \Rightarrow C = -\dfrac{g}{2k}$, so that

$$v = \frac{g}{2k}\left[(1 + kt) - \frac{1}{(1 + kt)}\right].$$

When the icicle reaches twice its initial mass $kt = 1$, so

$$v = \frac{3g}{4k}.$$

5

Worked example 5.4

A small hailstone falls from rest through a stationary cloud. Its mass m at time t is given by $m = Me^{kt}$, where M and k are constants.

Find the time when the hailstone reaches a speed of $\frac{g}{2k}$.

Solution

Applying the impulse–momentum principle, as in the previous example, gives

$$m\frac{dv}{dt} + v\frac{dm}{dt} = mg \qquad [1]$$

As $m = Me^{kt}$, we can find $\frac{dm}{dt}$.

$$\frac{dm}{dt} = kMe^{kt} = km$$

Now substituting for $\frac{dm}{dt}$ in equation [1] gives

$$m\frac{dv}{dt} + vmk = mg$$

$$\frac{dv}{dt} = g - kv$$

This differential equation can be solved as shown below.

$$\int \frac{1}{g - kv}\,dv = \int 1\,dt$$

$$-\frac{1}{k}\ln|g - kv| = t + c$$

As initially the hailstone is at rest we have $v = 0$ when $t = 0$, which gives

$$c = -\frac{1}{k}\ln g.$$

This then gives

$$-\frac{1}{k}\ln|g - kv| = t - \frac{1}{k}\ln g$$

or

$$\ln|g - kv| = \ln g - kt$$

Now we can substitute $v = \frac{g}{2k}$ and solve for t.

$$\ln\left|g - k\frac{g}{2k}\right| = \ln g - kt$$

$$\ln\left(\frac{g}{2}\right) = \ln g - kt$$

$$t = \frac{1}{k}\ln 2$$

EXERCISE 5B

1 A particle, P, of initial mass M_0 kg, falls vertically from rest, through a stationary cloud and increases in mass. If gravity is assumed constant, show that

$$m\frac{\mathrm{d}v}{\mathrm{d}t} + v\frac{\mathrm{d}m}{\mathrm{d}t} = mg,$$

where v is the velocity of the particle, and m is the mass of the particle at time t. In each of the following cases k is a constant and x is the distance that the particle has fallen at time t.

(a) If $\frac{\mathrm{d}m}{\mathrm{d}t} = kM_0$, find v as a function of t.

(b) If $\frac{\mathrm{d}m}{\mathrm{d}t} = km$, find v as a function of t.

(c) If $\frac{\mathrm{d}m}{\mathrm{d}t} = \lambda M_0 \mathrm{e}^{kt}$, find v as a function of t.

(d) If $m = M_0(1 + kx)$, find v^2 as a function of x.

(e) If $\frac{\mathrm{d}m}{\mathrm{d}t} = kmv$, find v^2 as a function of x.

$\left(\text{Hint: use } \frac{\mathrm{d}v}{\mathrm{d}t} = v\frac{\mathrm{d}v}{\mathrm{d}x}.\right)$

2 A small hailstone, of initial mass M_0, is modelled as a sphere of initial radius r_0, and falls from rest through a stationary cloud. The hailstone increases in mass, and gravity may be assumed to be constant throughout the motion. The radius of the hailstone, at time t, is r, and its speed is v. If $\frac{\mathrm{d}r}{\mathrm{d}t} = kr$ (k is constant), show that

$$\frac{\mathrm{d}v}{\mathrm{d}t} + 3kv = g.$$

(You may assume that the density of the hailstone is uniform.)

Find v as a function of t, and the maximum speed of the hailstone.

5

3 A large snowball, modelled as a sphere, rolls down a slope inclined at 30° to the horizontal. The ball picks up snow at a rate proportional to its speed and to its mass.

Letting $\frac{dm}{dt} = kmv$, and neglecting any resistance forces show that

$$2\frac{dv}{dt} + 2kv^2 = g.$$

Assuming that $v = 0$, when $x = 0$, solve the differential equation, to find v^2 as a function of x.

If the initial radius of the ball is 0.5 m, find the speed and distance travelled by the ball when its radius is 1 m.

4 A particle, of initial mass M_0, is projected vertically upwards with speed U. The particle picks up stationary mass as it rises such that at time t its mass is given by

$$m = M_0 e^{gt/U}.$$

If the acceleration due to gravity is assumed constant show that

$$v = U\left(2e^{-gt/U} - 1\right).$$

Find the mass of the particle when it reaches its highest point, and the maximum height reached above the point of projection.

5 A particle, of initial mass M_0, is projected vertically upwards with speed U. The particle picks up mass, which is travelling with speed U downwards, as it rises such that at time t its mass is given by

$$m = M_0 e^{gt/U}.$$

If the acceleration due to gravity is assumed constant show that

$$v = U\left(3e^{-gt/U} - 2\right).$$

Find the mass of the particle when it reaches its highest point, and the maximum height reached above the point of projection.

Key point summary

1 $\mathbf{F}\delta t$ = change in momentum in time δt p 89

This result is known as the impulse–momentum principle, which states that **the impulse of the resultant force on a particle is equal to the change of its linear momentum.**

Test yourself	What to review
1 A rocket, of initial mass M_0, is launched vertically upwards from rest at time $t = 0$. The mass of the rocket at time t s after launch is given by $$m = \tfrac{1}{2}M_0 + \tfrac{1}{2}M_0(1 - kt)$$ and burned fuel is ejected with speed U relative to the rocket. Find the speed of the rocket $\dfrac{1}{k}$ s after launch.	*Section 5.2*
2 A small icicle, of initial mass M_0, falls from rest through a stationary cloud. Its mass is m and its velocity is v, at time t s after it begins to fall. The mass of the icicle increases at a rate proportional to its mass, so that $\dfrac{\mathrm{d}m}{\mathrm{d}t} = km$. Find its velocity when it has been falling for t s.	*Section 5.3*
3 A raindrop falls from rest and its mass increases as it falls. At time t the mass of the raindrop is Me^{kt} . Find the speed of the raindrop when its mass has doubled.	*Section 5.3*

Test yourself ANSWERS

1 $v = U\ln 2 - \dfrac{g}{k}$.

2 $v = \dfrac{g}{k}\left(1 - e^{-kt}\right)$.

3 $\dfrac{g}{2k}$.

CHAPTER 6

Circular motion with variable speed

Learning objectives

After studying this chapter you should be able to:

- solve problems using the radial and tangential components of the acceleration
- use conservation of energy on problems where bodies move in vertical circles
- show the motion of a simple pendulum is simple harmonic for small amplitudes
- find the period of a simple pendulum.

6

6.1 Introduction

In the M2 or M3 module you will have studied circular motion, where bodies moved with a constant speed. In this chapter we will extend these ideas to bodies that move with variable speed. In the earlier module you saw that a body moving in a circle had an acceleration of magnitude $\frac{v^2}{r}$ or $r\omega^2$ directed towards the centre of the circle. We will see that there is still a component of the acceleration towards the centre of the circle but that there is now also a component along the tangent.

6.2 Circular motion at variable speed

In this section we will consider the acceleration of a particle following a circular path and apply the results to some simple examples.

The diagram shows a particle, P, that is following a circular path of radius r. The centre of the circle is at O and at time $t = 0$ the particle is at point A, so that $\angle AOP = \theta$.

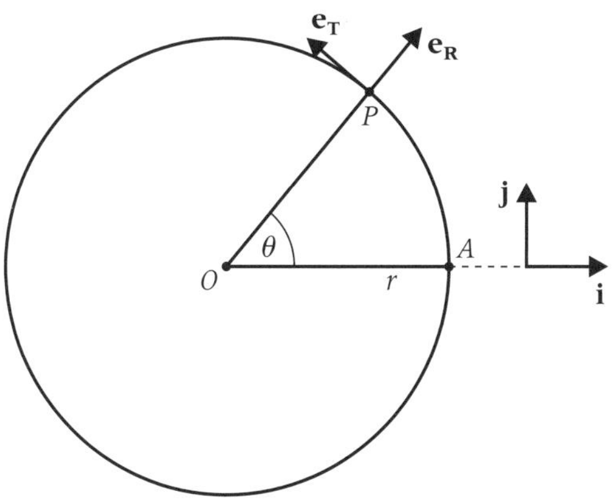

The diagram shows the unit vectors **i** and **j**. It also shows the unit vectors $\mathbf{e_R}$ and $\mathbf{e_T}$, which are directed along the radius and tangent of the circle at the current position of the particle. These unit vectors will be used to simplify the results that we obtain.

Using the unit vectors, **i** and **j**, the position vector, **r**, of the particle at time t is given by,

$$\mathbf{r} = r\cos\theta\,\mathbf{i} + r\sin\theta\,\mathbf{j}.$$

This can be differentiated to give the velocity of the particle as

$$\mathbf{v} = -r\sin\theta \times \frac{\mathrm{d}\theta}{\mathrm{d}t}\,\mathbf{i} + r\cos\theta\frac{\mathrm{d}\theta}{\mathrm{d}t}\,\mathbf{j}.$$

Note that using the chain rule gives

$$\frac{\mathrm{d}}{\mathrm{d}t}(\sin\theta) = \cos\theta \times \frac{\mathrm{d}\theta}{\mathrm{d}t}.$$

The velocity can then be differentiated, using the product rule, to give the acceleration.

$$\mathbf{a} = -r\left(\sin\theta\frac{\mathrm{d}^2\theta}{\mathrm{d}t^2} + \cos\theta\left(\frac{\mathrm{d}\theta}{\mathrm{d}t}\right)^2\right)\mathbf{i} + r\left(\cos\theta\frac{\mathrm{d}^2\theta}{\mathrm{d}t^2} - \sin\theta\left(\frac{\mathrm{d}\theta}{\mathrm{d}t}\right)^2\right)\mathbf{j}$$

These results can be simplified by using the unit vectors $\mathbf{e_R}$ and $\mathbf{e_T}$.

Note that

$$\mathbf{e_R} = \cos\theta\,\mathbf{i} + \sin\theta\,\mathbf{j}$$

and that

$$\mathbf{e_T} = -\sin\theta\,\mathbf{i} + \cos\theta\,\mathbf{j}.$$

Then the position vector becomes

$$\mathbf{r} = r\cos\theta\,\mathbf{i} + r\sin\theta\,\mathbf{j}$$
$$= r\mathbf{e_R}$$

That is, a vector of magnitude r directed outwards from the centre of the circle.
The velocity vector becomes

$$\mathbf{v} = -r\sin\theta \times \frac{\mathrm{d}\theta}{\mathrm{d}t}\mathbf{i} + r\cos\theta \times \frac{\mathrm{d}\theta}{\mathrm{d}t}\mathbf{j}$$
$$= r\frac{\mathrm{d}\theta}{\mathrm{d}t}\mathbf{e_T}$$

> The velocity is a vector of magnitude $r\frac{\mathrm{d}\theta}{\mathrm{d}t}$ directed along the tangent.

Now consider the acceleration.

$$\mathbf{a} = -r\left(\sin\theta\frac{d^2\theta}{dt^2} + \cos\theta\left(\frac{d\theta}{dt}\right)^2\right)\mathbf{i} + r\left(\cos\theta\frac{d^2\theta}{dt^2} - \sin\theta\left(\frac{d\theta}{dt}\right)^2\right)\mathbf{j}$$

$$= -r\left(\frac{d\theta}{dt}\right)^2(\cos\theta\,\mathbf{i} + \sin\theta\,\mathbf{j}) + r\frac{d^2\theta}{dt^2}(-\sin\theta\,\mathbf{i} + \cos\theta\,\mathbf{j})$$

$$= -r\left(\frac{d\theta}{dt}\right)^2\mathbf{e_R} + r\frac{d^2\theta}{dt^2}\,\mathbf{e_T}$$

The acceleration has a component of magnitude $r\left(\frac{d\theta}{dt}\right)^2$ directed towards the centre of the circle and a component of magnitude $r\frac{d^2\theta}{dt^2}$ directed along the tangent. These are often called the radial and transverse components of the acceleration.

It is also useful to be able to express these components of the acceleration in terms of v, the speed of the particle, using $v = r\frac{d\theta}{dt}$.

First consider the radial component of the acceleration.

$$r\left(\frac{d\theta}{dt}\right)^2 = \frac{1}{r}\left(r\frac{d\theta}{dt}\right)^2 = \frac{v^2}{r}$$

This expression for the radial component of the acceleration is the same for circular motion at constant speed.
Now consider the transverse component of the acceleration.

$$r\frac{d^2\theta}{dt^2} = \frac{d}{dt}\left(r\frac{d\theta}{dt}\right) = \frac{dv}{dt}$$

The radial component of the acceleration is $\frac{v^2}{r}$ and the transverse component is $\frac{dv}{dt}$.

These two results are applied in the following examples.

Worked example 6.1

A car, of mass 1200 kg, is travelling on a roundabout of radius 50 m. At the point P, it is travelling at $15\,\text{m s}^{-1}$ and its speed is increasing at $2\,\text{m s}^{-2}$.
Find the magnitude of the resultant force on the car:

(a) at the point P, **(b)** 5 s after it has left P.

Solution

(a) The car has a transverse component of acceleration of $2\,\mathrm{m\,s^{-2}}$.
The radial component of the acceleration is given by

$$\frac{v^2}{r} = \frac{15^2}{50} = 4.5\,\mathrm{m\,s^{-2}}.$$

The resultant of these two components will have magnitude

$$a = \sqrt{2^2 + 4.5^2} = 4.924\,\mathrm{m\,s^{-2}}.$$

The resultant force will then have magnitude

$$F = 1200 \times 4.924 = 5910\,\mathrm{N}\ (\text{to } 3\,\text{sf}).$$

(b) The transverse component of the acceleration of the car will still be $2\,\mathrm{m\,s^{-2}}$.
The speed of the car will now be

$$v = 15 + 2 \times 5 = 25\,\mathrm{m\,s^{-1}}.$$

The radial component of the acceleration can now be calculated.

$$\frac{v^2}{r} = \frac{25^2}{50} = 12.5\,\mathrm{m\,s^{-2}}$$

The magnitude of the resultant force on the car is then

$$F = 1200\sqrt{2^2 + 12.5^2} = 15\,200\,\mathrm{N}\ (\text{to } 3\text{sf})$$

Worked example 6.2

A car, of mass 1000 kg, is following a horizontal, circular path of radius 100 m. The coefficient of friction between the tyres of the car and the road is 0.7. Determine the maximum possible rate at which the speed of the car can increase, when it is travelling at $12\,\mathrm{m\,s^{-1}}$.

Solution

We begin by assuming that the friction is the only horizontal force that acts on the car. The friction force provides both the radial and transverse components of the resultant force.
The maximum value of the friction force will be

$$\begin{aligned} F &= \mu R \\ &= 0.7 \times 1000 \times 9.8 \\ &= 6860\,\mathrm{N} \end{aligned}$$

The radial component of the resultant force will have magnitude

$$\frac{mv^2}{r} = \frac{1000 \times 12^2}{100}$$
$$= 1440\,\text{N}$$

As the magnitude of the resultant force is a maximum the transverse component of the resultant force will be given by

$$\sqrt{6860^2 - 1440^2} = 6707\,\text{N (to 4 sf)}.$$

The maximum rate of increase of speed is then given by

$$\frac{6707}{1000} = 6.707\,\text{m s}^{-2}.$$

EXERCISE 6A

1 A car travels on a horizontal circular track of radius 150 m. The car's speed increases at a constant rate of $0.5\,\text{m s}^{-2}$. Find the total acceleration of the car after it has travelled a distance of 150 m from the point where its speed was $15\,\text{m s}^{-1}$.

2 A car is travelling on a horizontal road which is an arc of a circle of radius 400 m. The car is travelling at a speed of $30\,\text{m s}^{-1}$ when the brakes are applied so that the speed decreases at a rate of $1\,\text{m s}^{-2}$. Find the total acceleration of the car:

(a) immediately after the brakes have been applied,

(b) 5 s later.

3 A motorist is travelling on a circular track of radius 600 m and, when travelling at $35\,\text{m s}^{-1}$ applies his brakes so that, 10 s later, the car is moving with speed $25\,\text{m s}^{-1}$.

Assuming that the brakes produce a constant rate of decrease of speed, find the total acceleration of the car immediately after the brakes have been applied.

4 A car is travelling round a level road, which is an arc of a circle of radius 180 m. The speed of the car increases at the constant rate of $1.5\,\text{m s}^{-2}$ and the magnitude of the total acceleration of the car at point A is $2.5\,\text{m s}^{-2}$. Find the speed of the car at this point.

5 A heavy lorry starts off on a curve of 250 m radius and its speed increases at a constant rate of $0.6\,\text{m s}^{-2}$ from rest. Find the distance that the lorry will travel before its total acceleration reaches $0.8\,\text{m s}^{-2}$.

6 A particle, of mass m, can slide on a horizontal circular wire, of radius a, and the only force acting along the direction of motion is a force of constant magnitude $\frac{mV^2}{a}$ and opposing the motion.

(a) The particle is projected along the wire with speed $5V$. Find the distance that it travels before coming to rest.

(b) Find the initial acceleration of the particle.

7 A particle is threaded on a rough horizontal wire formed into a circle of radius a and is projected with angular speed Ω along the wire. The coefficient of friction between the particle and the wire is μ. Assuming that the vertical reaction of the wire may be neglected (i.e., the motion takes place in a gravity-free environment) find the total distance travelled by the particle in time t.

8 A particle, free to move on a horizontal table, is attached by a string of length a to a fixed point, A, of the table. The particle is projected, with the string taut, with speed u perpendicular to the string. After turning through one radian the string strikes a fixed peg at a distance b from A and subsequently the particle starts to describe a circle about the peg. Given that the coefficient of friction is μ, find the total time that the particle is in motion.

9 A car, of mass 1200 kg, is driven at $10\,\text{m s}^{-1}$ in a tight loop round a horizontal circle of radius 80 m. The tyres are limited to a total horizontal friction force of 10.6 kN. The driver then applies the brakes. What is the maximum possible deceleration?

10 Two particles, A and B, of mass m and $3m$, respectively, are on a rough horizontal table and joined by a light inextensible string. The coefficient of friction between either particle and the table is μ. Show that if particle A is projected perpendicularly to the string, which is initially taut, and particle B does not move in the subsequent motion, then the string cannot have turned through more than $\frac{3}{2}$ radians.

6.3 Motion in a vertical circle

In this section we will consider bodies that move in vertical circles, where the increases in the energy of the bodies are due to gravity. For example, a person on a rope swing moves in a part of a vertical circle, as does a roller coaster that 'loops the loop'. In these types of example the results for the acceleration of the body used in the previous section can still be applied, but it will also be necessary to use conservation of energy to determine the speed of the body.

Worked example 6.3

A child, of mass 50 kg, holds one end of a rope of length 3 m. The other end of the rope is tied to a tree branch. Initially the child stands, at rest, on a bank with the rope horizontal. The child then swings on the rope and follows a circular path in a vertical plane.

(a) Find the tension in the rope when the rope is at angle θ to the vertical.

(b) Find the maximum tension in the rope and describe the position of the child when the tension is a maximum.

Solution

(a) The diagram shows the position of the child and the angle θ. The speed of the child can be determined using conservation of energy.

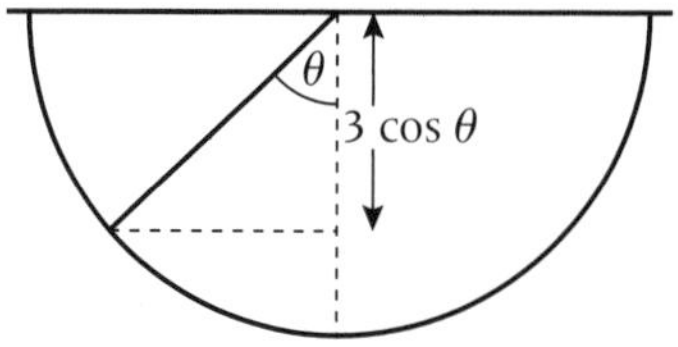

$$\text{Potentital energy lost} = 50 \times 9.8 \times 3\cos\theta = 1470\cos\theta$$

$$\frac{1}{2} \times 50v^2 = 1470\cos\theta$$

$$v^2 = \frac{1470}{25}\cos\theta$$

Now consider the forces acting on the child. These are shown in the diagram.
Resolving radially and applying Newton's second law gives

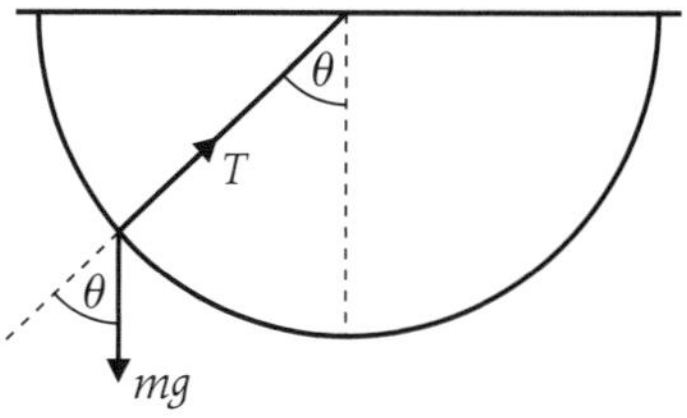

$$T - mg\cos\theta = \frac{mv^2}{r}.$$

Substituting the values for the mass and radius gives

$$T - 490\cos\theta = \frac{50v^2}{3}$$

The expression for v^2 obtained earlier can now be substituted.

$$T - 490\cos\theta = \frac{50}{3} \times \frac{1470}{25}\cos\theta$$

$$T = 1470\cos\theta$$

(b) As $\cos\theta$ has a maximum of 1 when $\theta = 0°$, the tension will have its maximum value when the position of the child corresponds to this value of θ. Referring back to the diagram it can be seen that $\theta = 0°$ when the rope is vertical and the child is at the lowest position.

Worked example 6.4

A particle, of mass 5 kg, is placed at the point A at the top of a hemisphere, of radius 2 m and centre O. The hemisphere is fixed to a horizontal surface, as shown in the diagram. The particle is set into motion with an initial horizontal speed of 3 m s^{-1}. The particle leaves the surface of the hemisphere at the point B. Find the angle AOB.

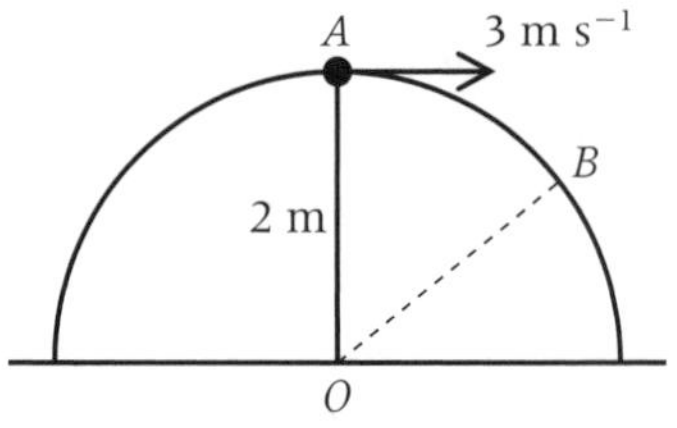

Solution

The diagram shows the forces acting on the particle and the angle θ.

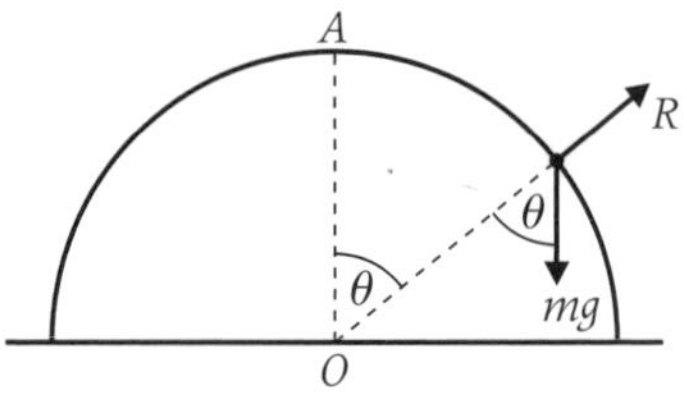

Using conservation of energy the speed of the particle at the point shown can be determined.

$$\text{Potential energy lost} = 5 \times 9.8 \times (2 - 2\cos\theta) = 98(1 - \cos\theta)$$

As this will be equal to the gain in kinetic energy, we have

$$98(1 - \cos\theta) = \frac{1}{2} \times 5v^2 - \frac{1}{2} \times 5 \times 3^2$$

$$v^2 = 39.2(1 - \cos\theta) + 9$$

Resolving radially at the point shown in the diagram and applying Newton's second law gives

$$5g\cos\theta - R = \frac{5v^2}{2}$$

$$R = 5g\cos\theta - \frac{5v^2}{2}$$

The particle will leave the surface when $R = 0$. This can be expressed in terms of the speed of the particle as

$$0 = 5g\cos\theta - \frac{5v^2}{2}$$

$$v^2 = 2g\cos\theta$$

Now this result can be substituted into the expression for the speed obtained by considering energy, to give the required angle.

$$19.6\cos\theta = 39.2(1 - \cos\theta) + 9$$

$$\cos\theta = \frac{39.2 + 9}{19.6 + 39.2}$$

$$\theta = 34.9°$$

Worked example 6.5

A toy car is released from rest on the loop-the-loop track shown in the diagram. The loop has a diameter of 50 cm. Determine the minimum height, h, from which the car must be released if the car is to loop the loop.

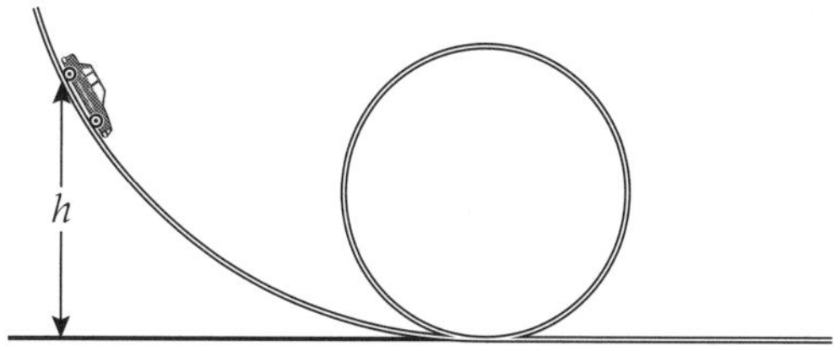

Solution

For the car to loop the loop it must remain in contact with the track at all times. The diagram shows the forces acting on the car.

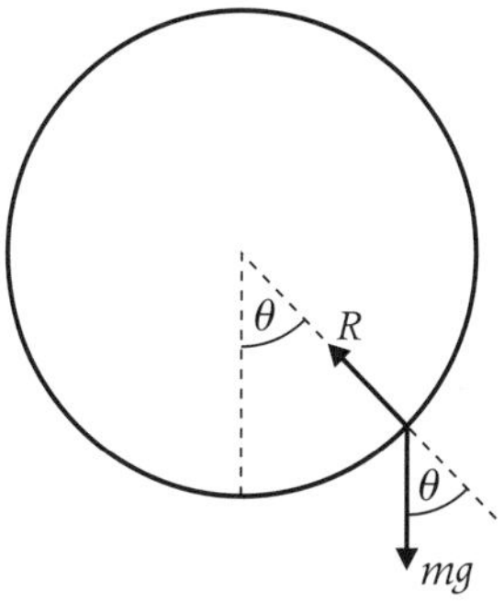

Resolving radially and applying Newton's second law gives

$$R - mg\cos\theta = \frac{mv^2}{r}.$$

If the car stays in contact with the track at any point

$$R \geqslant 0$$

$$\frac{mv^2}{r} + mg\cos\theta \geqslant 0$$

$$v^2 \geqslant -rg\cos\theta$$

Note that $\cos\theta$ varies between -1 and 1, so that taking $\theta = 180^\circ$, for which $\cos\theta = -1$, gives

$$v^2 \geqslant rg.$$

This means that the minimum speed of the car at the top of the loop is $\sqrt{rg}$ or $\sqrt{0.25 \times 9.8} = \sqrt{2.45}$.

Now conservation of energy can be used to find the initial height of the car, as the total energy at the top of the loop must be equal to the total initial energy.

$$mgh = \frac{1}{2}mv^2 + mg \times 2r$$

Using the values for v obtained above and the radius of the circle gives

$$9.8h = \frac{1}{2} \times 2.45 + 9.8 \times 0.5$$

$$h = 0.625\,\text{m}$$

6

When attempting problems involving vertical circular motion:

- use conservation of energy to find the speed of the object in the required position,
- resolve radially and apply Newton's second law.

EXERCISE 6B

1 A soldier, of mass 75 kg, swings on a light inextensible rope of length 6 m. The soldier is initially at rest and the angle between the rope and the vertical is 30°.

(a) Find the maximum speed of the soldier and the tension in rope at that time.

(b) Find the tension in the rope when the rope is at an angle of 20° to the vertical.

2 A bead is threaded onto a smooth vertical hoop of radius 2 m. The mass of the bead is 0.05 kg.

(a) If the speed of the bead is $10\,\text{m s}^{-1}$ at the lowest point of the hoop, find the speed of the bead at the top of the hoop and the force that the hoop exerts on the bead in this position.

(b) Determine the force exerted on the bead by the hoop at the lowest point of the hoop.

3 An eskimo, of mass 60 kg, sits on the top of his igloo. The igloo is assumed to be a smooth hemisphere of radius 3 m. The eskimo is pushed so that he initially moves horizontally at $0.5\,\text{m s}^{-1}$. The diagram shows the angle θ when the eskimo is at the point P.

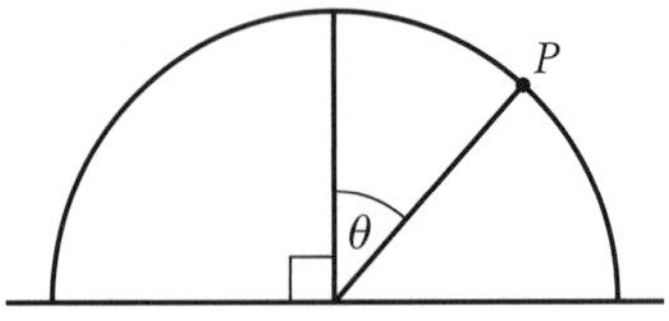

(a) Find the reaction force exerted on the eskimo when $\theta = 10°$.

(b) Show that the eskimo leaves the surface of the igloo and find the value of θ when this happens.

4 A child, of mass 35 kg, sits on a swing and swings freely through an angle of 30° on either side of the vertical. The ropes of the swing are 2.5 m long. Modelling the motion as that of a particle of mass 35 kg attached to an inextensible rope of length 2.5 m find the speed of the child when the rope is vertical and also the tension in the rope at that instant.

5 An aeroplane is flown at a constant speed of $175\,\text{m s}^{-1}$ in a vertical circle of radius 1000 m. Find the force exerted by the seat on the pilot, of mass 80 kg, at the lowest and highest points.

6 A man swings a bucket full of water in a vertical plane in a circle of radius 0.5 m. What is the smallest velocity that the bucket should have at the top of the circle if no water is to be spilt?

7 The diagram shows the rotating drum of a spin dryer. The radius of the drum is 0.3 m. Find the angular velocity of the drum so that a small article of clothing drops off the drum when $\theta = 40°$. You may assume that the surface of the drum is such as to prevent slipping before loss of contact.

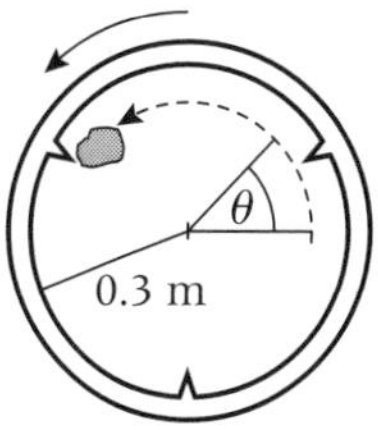

8 A bead, of mass m, is threaded on a smooth circular loop of wire of radius a and which is fixed in a vertical plane. The bead is released from rest at the end of a horizontal diameter. Find the reaction of the wire when the bead has turned through an angle θ.

9 A particle is released from rest at a point on the outer surface of a smooth sphere of radius a; the point of release is at height $\frac{a}{2}$ above the centre. Find the height above the centre at which the particle leaves the sphere.

10 On a child's toy, a small car is fired along a smooth track and loops the loop inside a section of track fixed in the form of a vertical circle of radius a and centre O, as shown in the diagram.

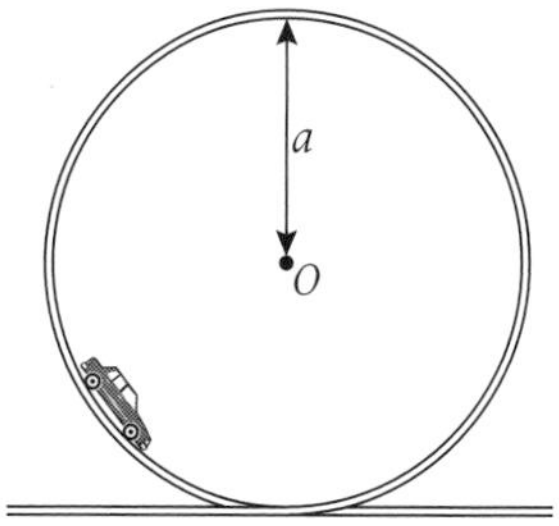

The car is travelling at speed u as it enters the circle at the lowest point. Modelling the car as a particle P, of mass m, find the reaction of the track on the particle in terms of m, g, a, θ and u when OP makes an angle θ with the downward vertical.

Deduce that the car will complete the vertical circle if $u > \sqrt{5ga}$. [A]

11 A bead, of mass m, is threaded onto a smooth circular ring, of radius r, which is fixed in a vertical plane. The bead is moving on the wire so that its speed, v, at the highest point of its path is half of its speed at the lowest point.

(a) Find v in terms of r and g.

(b) Find the reaction of the wire on the bead, in terms of m and g, when the bead is
(i) at the highest point,
(ii) $\frac{1}{2}r$ above its lowest point. [A]

12 James and Emma are carrying out separate experiments, using two identical particles. James attaches his particle to a light inelastic string of length l.

Emma threads her particle onto a smooth ring, of radius l, which is fixed in a vertical plane. James and Emma then measure the minimum speed, at the lowest point, necessary for the particle to be able to make complete circles in a vertical plane.

(a) What should James find to be the minimum speed?

(b) What should be the difference between the two speeds which they find? [A]

6.4 The simple pendulum

In this section we will consider the motion of the simple pendulum and show that for small angles this motion is approximately simple harmonic.

The simple pendulum consists of a particle fixed to one end of a light inextensible string that swings on an arc of a circle in a vertical plane. To analyse the motion of the simple pendulum consider the simple pendulum shown in the diagram. The pendulum bob has mass m and the length of the string is l.

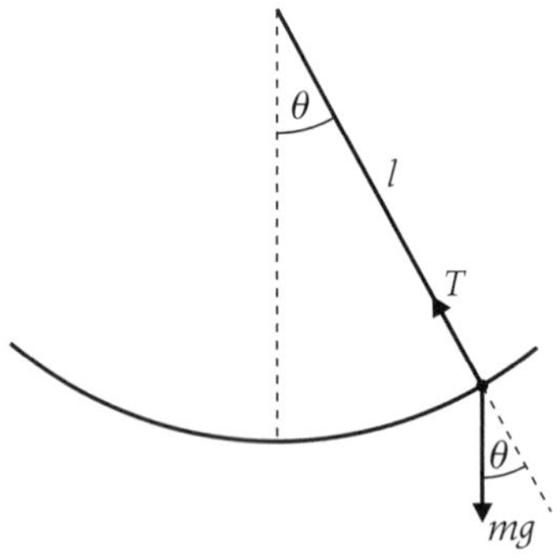

The tension has no transverse component and so will not affect the speed of the pendulum. The transverse component of the weight of the pendulum is $-mg\sin\theta$.

In section 6.2 we found that the transverse component of acceleration for a body following a circular path is $r\frac{d^2\theta}{dt^2}$, so applying Newton's second law in the transverse direction gives

$$ml\frac{d^2\theta}{dt^2} = -mg\sin\theta$$

$$\frac{d^2\theta}{dt^2} = -\frac{g\sin\theta}{l}$$

Now we need to consider the $\sin\theta$ term in this equation of motion. When θ is small we can use the approximation $\sin\theta \approx \theta$.

For small angles the equation of motion for a simple pendulum is

$$\frac{d^2\theta}{dt^2} = -\frac{g}{l}\theta.$$

You will recall from the M2 module that for simple harmonic motion we require that $\frac{d^2x}{dt^2} = -\omega^2 x$. The equation for the simple pendulum satisfies this condition for small values of θ. In this case $\omega = \sqrt{\frac{g}{l}}$.

You will also recall that the period of the motion is given by $T = \frac{2\pi}{\omega}$.

> The period of a simple pendulum is given by
>
> $$T = 2\pi\sqrt{\frac{l}{g}}.$$

Worked example 6.6

A simple pendulum has a string of length 50 cm. Show that the pendulum moves with simple harmonic motion and find the period of the pendulum.

Solution

The transverse component of the weight of the pendulum is $-mg\sin\theta$ or $-mg\,\theta$ if the values of θ are small and where m is the mass of the pendulum. The transverse component of the acceleration of the pendulum is $0.5\frac{d^2\theta}{dt^2}$.

Applying Newton's second law gives

$$m \times 0.5\frac{d^2\theta}{dt^2} = -mg\theta$$

$$\frac{d^2\theta}{dt^2} = -2g\theta$$

So the motion will be simple harmonic provided that θ is small.

The period of the motion will be

$$T = \frac{2\pi}{\sqrt{2g}} = 1.42\text{ s}.$$

Worked example 6.7

The diagram shows the path of a particle attached to a light string. The particle is initially at A, and swings in an arc of radius $2a$ to B. The string then comes into contact with a peg, P, and the particle then swings in an arc of radius a. Find the time that it takes for the particle to swing from A to C.

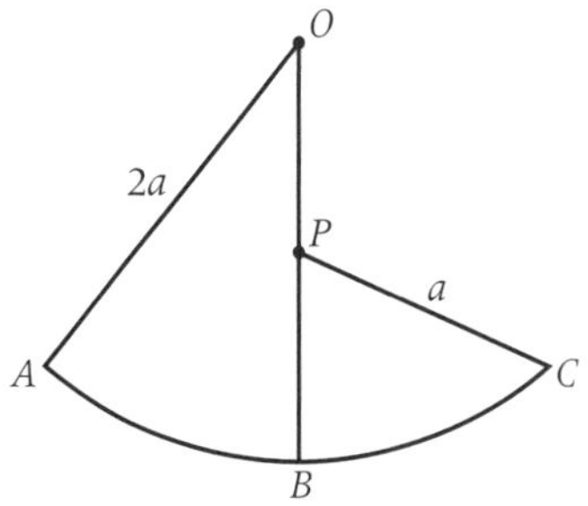

Solution

As the particle swings from A to B it moves with simple harmonic motion governed by the equation

$$\frac{d^2\theta}{dt^2} = -\frac{g}{2a}\theta.$$

The time, T_1, taken to move from A to B is $\frac{1}{4}$ of the period, that is

$$T_1 = \frac{1}{4} \times 2\pi\sqrt{\frac{2a}{g}} = \frac{\sqrt{2}}{2}\pi\sqrt{\frac{a}{g}}.$$

Similarly, for the motion from B to C, $\dfrac{d^2\theta}{dt^2} = -\dfrac{g}{a}\theta.$

So the time, T_2, to move from B to C, is

$$T_2 = \frac{1}{4} \times 2\pi\sqrt{\frac{a}{g}} = \frac{1}{2}\pi\sqrt{\frac{a}{g}}.$$

$$\text{Total time} = T_1 + T_2 = \frac{(1+\sqrt{2})\pi}{2}\sqrt{\frac{a}{g}}.$$

Worked example 6.8

A simple pendulum has length 0.8 m. It is released from rest with the string at an angle of $\frac{\pi}{20}$ to the vertical.

(a) Find an expression for angle between the string and the vertical at time t s.

(b) Find the time that it takes for the angle between the string and the vertical to be reduced to $\frac{\pi}{40}$.

Solution

(a) The pendulum will move with simple harmonic motion, so at time t the angle θ will be given by

$$\theta = A\cos(\omega t + \alpha).$$

For a simple pendulum we have $\dfrac{d^2\theta}{dt^2} = -\dfrac{g}{l}\theta$, so that

$$\omega = \sqrt{\frac{9.8}{0.8}} = \frac{7}{2}.$$

Initially $\dfrac{d\theta}{dt} = 0$ and at time t, $\dfrac{d\theta}{dt} = -A\omega\sin(\omega t + \alpha)$, so

$$0 = -A\sin\alpha$$

$$\alpha = 0$$

Also as the angle is initially $\frac{\pi}{20}$ we have

$$\frac{\pi}{20} = A\cos(0)$$
$$A = \frac{\pi}{20}$$

The angle between the string and the vertical at time t is

$$\theta = \frac{\pi}{20}\cos\left(\frac{7t}{2}\right).$$

(b) We need to find the time when $\theta = \frac{\pi}{40}$ for the first time.

$$\frac{\pi}{10} = \frac{\pi}{20}\cos\left(\frac{7t}{2}\right)$$
$$\frac{1}{2} = \cos\left(\frac{7t}{2}\right)$$
$$\frac{7t}{2} = \frac{\pi}{3}$$
$$t = \frac{2\pi}{21}$$

EXERCISE 6C

1 A simple pendulum has a period of 0.8 s. Find the length of the pendulum.

2 A DIY magazine claims that a clock that is fast (i.e., gaining time) can be slowed down by sticking a small lump of Blu-tack to the back of the pendulum. Comment on this procedure.

3 A clock manufacture wishes to produce a clock operated by a pendulum. It has been decided that a pendulum of length 15 cm will fit well into an available clock casing. Find the period of this pendulum, assuming that it is a simple pendulum.

4 A clock regulated by a pendulum gains 10 minutes every day. How should the pendulum be altered to correct the timekeeping of the clock?

5 Two identical simple pendulums are set into motion. One is released from rest and the other with a push, both from the same initial position. How do the amplitude and period of the subsequent motions compare?

6 The pendulums in Question **5** have strings of length 20 cm. Find expressions for the angle between the string and the vertical if they were initially at an angle of 5° to the vertical and the one that was pushed was given an initial velocity of $0.5\,\mathrm{m\,s^{-1}}$.

7 A seconds pendulum is such that it takes one second for the pendulum to swing from one end of its path to the other end, i.e., each half of the oscillation takes 1 s.

(a) Find the length of the seconds pendulum.

(b) A seconds pendulum is found to gain one minute per day. Find the necessary change in length of the pendulum if the pendulum is to be made accurate.

8 A simple pendulum oscillates with period $2t$ s. By what percentage should the pendulum length be shortened so that it has a period of t s?

9 A simple pendulum has length 3 m. The pendulum is released from rest with the string at an angle of $\frac{\pi}{30}$ to the vertical.

(a) Find an expression for the angle between the string and the vertical at time t.

(b) Find the time that it takes for the pendulum to swing through an angle of $\frac{\pi}{40}$ from its initial position.

10 A simple pendulum has period $\frac{\pi}{10}$ s and is initially at rest with the string at an angle of $\frac{\pi}{50}$ to the vertical.

(a) Find an expression for the angle between the string and the vertical at time t s.

(b) Find an expression for the transverse component of the velocity of the pendulum bob at time t s.

11 A simple pendulum consists of a mass on the end of a string of length $2a$.

(a) Draw a diagram to show the forces acting on the mass when the string is inclined at an angle θ to the vertical.

(b) By considering the component of the resultant force perpendicular to the string show that at time t

$$\frac{\mathrm{d}^2\theta}{\mathrm{d}t^2} \approx -\frac{g\theta}{2a}$$

stating clearly any assumptions you have made.

(c) Find the period of the simple pendulum in terms of a, g and π.

(d) The pendulum swings through a small angle from A, where it was at rest, to C, where it comes to rest again. It describes an arc of radius $2a$ between A and B, and an arc of radius a between B and C.

Find the time that it takes for the pendulum to get from A to C. [A]

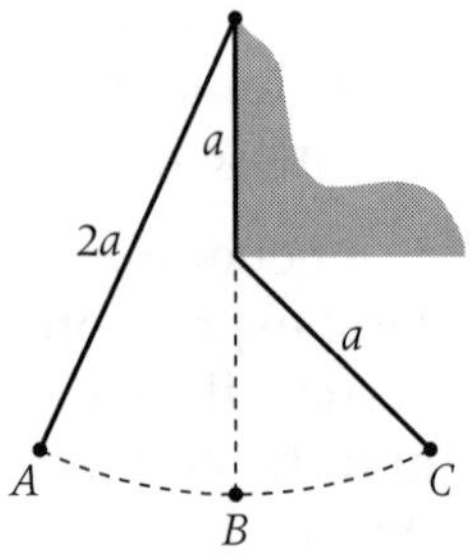

12 *In this question you may assume that the motion of a simple pendulum can be modelled by the differential equation* $\frac{d^2\theta}{dt^2} = -\frac{g\theta}{l}$, *where* θ *is the angle, in radians, between the string and the vertical at time* t *s and* l *is the length of the string in metres.*

A simple pendulum has a string of length 40 cm.

(a) Find the period of this pendulum, using $g = 9.8\,\text{m s}^{-2}$.

The pendulum is taken to a place at a different altitude and it is found that its period changes to 1.3 s.

(b) Find the value of g at this altitude.

(c) State whether the altitude at which the pendulum is situated in **(b)** has increased or decreased from that in **(a)**, giving a reason to support your answer. [A]

Key point summary

1 The velocity is a vector of magnitude $r\frac{d\theta}{dt}$ directed along the tangent. *p 102*

2 The acceleration has a component of magnitude $r\left(\frac{d\theta}{dt}\right)^2$ directed towards the centre of the circle and a component of magnitude $r\frac{d^2\theta}{dt^2}$ directed along the tangent. These are often called the radial and transverse components of the acceleration. *p 103*

3 The radial component of the acceleration is $\frac{v^2}{r}$ and the transverse component is $\frac{dv}{dt}$. *p 103*

4 When attempting problems involving vertical circular motion: *p 110*

- use conservation of energy to find the speed of the object in the required position,
- resolve radially and apply Newton's second law.

5 For small angles the equation of motion for a simple pendulum is *p 112*

$$\frac{d^2\theta}{dt^2} = -\frac{g}{l}\theta.$$

6 The period of a simple pendulum is given by *p 113*

$$T = 2\pi\sqrt{\frac{l}{g}}.$$

6

Test yourself — What to review

1 A car, of mass 1200 kg, follows a circular path of radius 120 m. The speed of the car is increasing at $0.5\,\text{m}\,\text{s}^{-2}$. Find the magnitude of the resultant force on the car when it is travelling at $10\,\text{m}\,\text{s}^{-1}$. — *Section 6.2*

2 A bead, P, of mass m, is threaded onto a smooth circular hoop of radius 0.75 m and centre O. The bead is set into motion with a speed of $3\,\text{m}\,\text{s}^{-1}$ at the top of the hoop. — *Section 6.3*

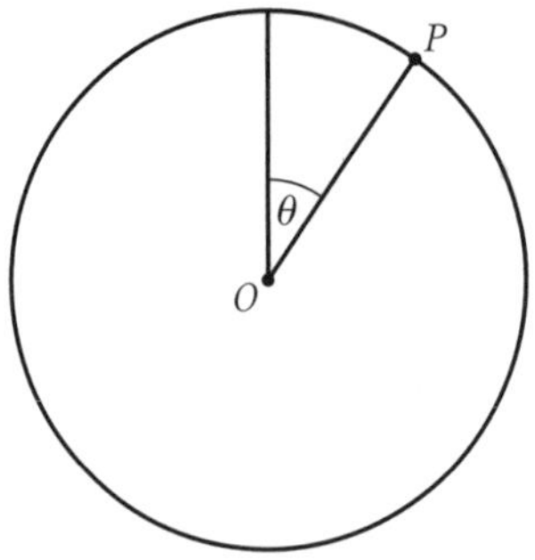

(a) Find the speed of the bead when it is in the position shown in the diagram.

(b) Find the position of the bead when the reaction force exerted on the bead by the hoop is equal to half of the reaction force exerted by the hoop on the bead at its lowest point.

3 A simple pendulum has a string of length 60 cm and is released from rest. Find the time that it takes for the angle between the string and the vertical to be reduced to $\frac{1}{3}$ of its initial value. — *Section 6.4*

Test yourself ANSWERS

1 1166 N.

2 **(a)** $v = \sqrt{9 + 14.7(1 - \cos\theta)}$; **(b)** 87.9°.

3 0.305 s.

Exam style practice paper

Time allowed 1 hour 15 minutes

Answer **all** questions

---

1 Find the acute angle between the forces $\mathbf{F}_1 = 2\mathbf{i} + 3\mathbf{j} - 6\mathbf{k}$ and $\mathbf{F}_2 = \mathbf{i} + 2\mathbf{j} + 2\mathbf{k}$. *(3 marks)*

2 The forces $\mathbf{F}_1 = 4\mathbf{i} + 3\mathbf{j} + 2\mathbf{k}$ and $\mathbf{F}_2 = 2\mathbf{i} - \mathbf{j} + 2\mathbf{k}$ act at the points with coordinates (4, 5, 5) and (0, 0, 2), respectively. The unit vectors **i**, **j** and **k** are directed along the x, y and z axes respectively.

The forces $\mathbf{F}_1$ and $\mathbf{F}_2$ are equivalent to a third force, **F**, that acts at the origin and a couple **G**. Find **F** and **G**. *(6 marks)*

3 A golf ball is hit on a fairway, which is at an angle of 5° to the horizontal. The ball moves in a vertical plane that includes the line of greatest slope of the fairway. The ball is hit so that it initially moves at $30\,\mathrm{m\,s^{-1}}$ and at an angle of 50° above the fairway. The ball moves down the slope of the fairway.

(a) Find the time of flight of the ball. *(4 marks)*

(b) Find the range of the ball, to the nearest metre. *(4 marks)*

(c) Find the speed of the ball when it hits the ground. *(3 marks)*

4 A ball is travelling horizontally when it hits a vertical wall. The ball is in contact with the wall for 0.4 s and rebounds travelling horizontally. The magnitude of the reaction force, R N, which acts on the ball, is modelled as

$$R = 40t(0.4 - t) \qquad 0 \leqslant t \leqslant 0.4$$

where t is the time since the ball hit the wall.

(a) Find the magnitude of the impulse of the ball. *(5 marks)*

The ball is travelling at $8\,\mathrm{m\,s^{-1}}$ when it hits the wall and rebounds at $5\,\mathrm{m\,s^{-1}}$.

(b) Determine the mass of the ball. *(3 marks)*

5 A particle, P, is initially at rest, on the top of a hemisphere, of radius a and centre O. The particle is released from rest. When the particle moves the angle between OP and the vertical is θ.

(a) Show that the speed, v, of the particle is given by

$\sqrt{2ga(1 - \cos\theta)}$. *(4 marks)*

(b) Find the speed of the particle when it leaves the surface of the hemisphere, giving your answer in terms of a and g. *(6 marks)*

6 A spring has natural length l and modulus of elasticity λ. One end of the spring is fixed at O, and the other attached to a block of mass m. The whole system is arranged on a smooth horizontal surface, as shown in the diagram.

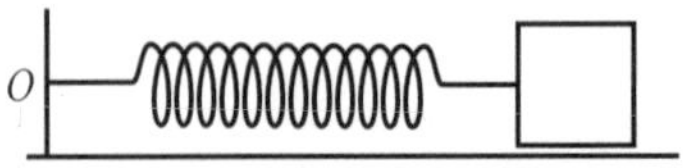

Initially the block is moved towards O so that the spring is compressed to half of its natural length and released from rest. The displacement of the block from its equilibrium position at time t is x. As the block moves it experiences a resistance force that has magnitude cv, where c is a constant and v the speed of the block at time t.

(a) Show that $m\dfrac{d^2x}{dt^2} + c\dfrac{dx}{dt} + \dfrac{\lambda x}{l} = 0$. *(3 marks)*

(b) Given that $c = 2\sqrt{\dfrac{m\lambda}{l}}$ describe the motion that takes place. *(3 marks)*

(c) Find an expression for x at time t. *(5 marks)*

7 A rocket is initially at rest on the surface of the earth. It ejects burned fuel at a speed of U relative to the rocket. The mass of the rocket at time t is given by $m = M\left(1 - \dfrac{3t}{400}\right)$ for $0 \leqslant t \leqslant 100$.

The rocket runs out of fuel when $t = 100$. The velocity of the rocket at time t is v.

(a) Show that $\dfrac{dv}{dt} = \dfrac{3U}{400 - 3t} - g$. *(5 marks)*

(b) Find the speed of the rocket when it runs out of fuel, giving your answers in terms of U and g. *(6 marks)*

Answers

1 Vector methods in mechanics

EXERCISE 1A

1 **(a)** -49; **(b)** -6; **(c)** -41; **(d)** -3.

2 **(a)** $92.9°$; **(b)** $127.6°$; **(c)** $102.6°$; **(d)** $131.8°$.

3 **(a)** 10J; **(b)** $\sqrt{5}\ \text{m s}^{-1}$.

4 **(a)** -19J; **(b)** $2.28\ \text{m s}^{-1}$.

5 2J. **6** 42J. **7** $\lambda = -1$.

8 $\lambda = \frac{16}{3}$. **9** $-4, \frac{836}{155}$. **10** $-8, 4$.

11 **(a)** $\sqrt{29}$ N, $2\mathbf{i} - \mathbf{j} + 1.5\mathbf{k}$; **(b)** $80.7°$.

12 **(a)** $-90\mathbf{i} + 120\mathbf{j} + 140\mathbf{k}$; 205 N; **(b)** $69.8°$.

13 **(a)** $8\mathbf{i} + 4\mathbf{j} + 2\mathbf{k}$; **(b)** $11.5°$; **(c)** 80 N.

EXERCISE 1B

1 **(a)** $5\mathbf{i} + 29\mathbf{j} + 31\mathbf{k}$; **(b)** $-\mathbf{i} - 6\mathbf{j} - 5\mathbf{k}$;
(c) $-21\mathbf{i} + 11\mathbf{j} + 8\mathbf{k}$; **(d)** $-9\mathbf{i} + 6\mathbf{j} + 15\mathbf{k}$.

2 **(a)** $\frac{\sqrt{802}}{30}$; **(b)** $\sqrt{\frac{375}{377}}$; **(c)** $\sqrt{\frac{385}{513}}$; **(d)** $\frac{1}{\sqrt{51}}$.

EXERCISE 1C

1 $45\mathbf{k}$. **2** $38\mathbf{k}$.

3 $25\mathbf{k}$. **4** $-16\mathbf{i} - 34\mathbf{j} + 29\mathbf{k}$.

5 $9\mathbf{k}$. **6** $-50\mathbf{i} - 45\mathbf{j} - 140\mathbf{k}$.

7 $-25\mathbf{k}$. **8** $-26\mathbf{i} + 14\mathbf{j} + 37\mathbf{k}$.

EXERCISE 1D

1 $19\mathbf{i} + 5\mathbf{j}$, $19y = 5x + 84$. **2** $13\mathbf{i} + 5\mathbf{j}$, $13y = 5x + 1$.

3 $10\mathbf{i} + 24\mathbf{j}$, $5y = 12x + 31$. **4** $12\mathbf{i} + 9\mathbf{j}$, $12y = 9x - 31$.

5 **(a)** $\mathbf{F} = \mathbf{i} + 8\mathbf{j}$, $\mathbf{G} = -30\mathbf{i} + 9\mathbf{j} + 18\mathbf{k}$; **(b)** $\sqrt{\frac{83}{23}}$.

6 **(a)** $\mathbf{F} = 9\mathbf{i} + 6\mathbf{j} - 6\mathbf{k}$, $\mathbf{G} = -121\mathbf{i} + 66\mathbf{j} - 16\mathbf{k}$; **(b)** $9\sqrt{\frac{34}{83}}$.

7 **(a)** $\mathbf{F} = 13\mathbf{i} + 5\mathbf{j} - \mathbf{k}$, $\mathbf{G} = 7\mathbf{i} + 74\mathbf{j} - 18\mathbf{k}$; **(b)** $\sqrt{\frac{783}{19}}$.

8 **(a)** $\mathbf{F} = 6\mathbf{i} + 5\mathbf{j} - 4\mathbf{k}$, $\mathbf{G} = -44\mathbf{i} + 62\mathbf{j} - 67\mathbf{k}$; **(b)** $\sqrt{\frac{16\,390}{61}}$.

9 48 N m in sense *ABCD*.

10 **k**.

11 **(a)** 5; **(b)** $\mathbf{r} = \mathbf{i} + 2\mathbf{j} + \mathbf{k} + \lambda(7\mathbf{i} + 6\mathbf{j} + 6\mathbf{k})$; **(c)** $6\mathbf{i} + \mathbf{j} - 8\mathbf{k}$.

12 **(a)** $\frac{4\sqrt{3}}{3}$; **(b)** $\mathbf{R} = (3\mathbf{i} + 3\mathbf{k})$ N, $\mathbf{G} = -(\mathbf{i} + 2\mathbf{j} + 3\mathbf{k})$;
(c) $-(1 + 3y)\mathbf{i} - (3(z - x) + 2)\mathbf{j} + (3y - 3)\mathbf{k}$.

13 **(a)** $-\mathbf{i} + 7\mathbf{j}$, $\left(\frac{5}{7}, 0\right)$; **(b)** 2 N m.

14 **(a)** $8\mathbf{i} + 5\mathbf{k}$; **(b)** $2\mathbf{i} - 8\mathbf{k}$; **(c)** $-8\mathbf{i} - 5\mathbf{k}$, (0, 1, 0).

2 The motion of a projectile on an inclined plane

EXERCISE 2A

1 **(a)** 1.24 s; **(b)** 11.6 s; **(c)** 1.87 m.

2 **(a)** 22.6 m; **(b)** 21.6 m, a difference of about 5%.

3 122 m. **4** 32.3%. **5** 143.2 m, 181.5 m.

6 $\frac{2V^2 \sin\theta \cos(\theta - \alpha)}{g \cos^2\alpha}$.

8 **(c)** $\theta = \frac{90 - \alpha}{2}$.

9 $\frac{2V^2 \sin(\theta - \alpha) \cos\theta}{g \cos^2\alpha}$.

10 7.88 m s^{-1}. **11** $\theta < 53.9°$. **12** 8.85 m s^{-1}. **13** **(b)** $\frac{2U^2}{3g}$.

3 Forced and damped harmonic motion

EXERCISE 3A

1 **(a)** $x = Ae^{-t} + Be^{-6t}$ heavy;
(b) $x = (A + Bt)e^{-3t}$ critical;
(c) $x = Ae^{-4t} + Be^{-3t}$ heavy;
(d) $x = e^{-2t}(A\cos 3t + B\sin 3t)$ light;

(e) $x = e^{-\frac{5}{2}t}\left(A\cos\frac{3}{2}t + B\sin\frac{3}{2}t\right)$ light;

(f) $x = (A + Bt)e^{-\frac{5}{2}t}$ critical.

2 (a) $x = 5e^{-t} - 5e^{-2t}$ heavy;

(b) $x = \frac{10}{3}e^{-t} - \frac{1}{3}e^{-10t}$ heavy;

(c) $x = 8(1 + 2t)e^{-2t}$ critical;

(d) $x = e^{-\frac{5}{2}t}\left(3\cos\frac{\sqrt{3}}{2}t + 5\sqrt{3}\sin\frac{\sqrt{3}}{2}t\right)$ light;

(e) $x = \frac{4\sqrt{5}}{5}e^{-t}\sin\sqrt{5}t$ light;

(f) $x = e^{-\frac{t}{2}}\left(2\cos\frac{\sqrt{11}}{2}t + \frac{2}{\sqrt{11}}\sin\frac{\sqrt{11}}{2}t\right)$ light.

3 $x = ae^{-nt}(\cos 3nt - 3\sin 3nt)$.

4 $x = \frac{u}{n}e^{-nt}\sin nt,\ e^{-\pi}$.

5 (c) (ii) $x = e^{-bt}\left(A\cos\sqrt{\omega^2 - b^2}t + B\sin\sqrt{\omega^2 - b^2}t\right)$, **(iii)** $b > \omega$.

EXERCISE 3B

1 (a) $x = Ae^{-t} + Be^{-6t} + 2$;

(b) $x = (A + Bt)e^{-3t} + \frac{14}{27} - \frac{4}{27}t + \frac{1}{9}t^2$;

(c) $x = Ae^{-t} + Be^{-5t} - 2e^{-2t}$;

(d) $x = e^{-2t}(A\cos 3t + B\sin 3t) + \frac{1}{2}e^{-t}$;

(e) $x = A\cos 3t + B\sin 3t + \frac{1}{5}\cos 2t + \frac{3}{5}\sin 2t$;

(f) $x = A\cos 7t + B\sin 7t + \frac{2}{7}t\sin 7t$.

2 (a) $x = 4 - 4e^{-t}\cos t$;

(b) $x = \frac{17}{2}e^{-2t} - \frac{7}{2}e^{-4t} + 3te^{-2t}$;

(c) $x = (5 + 25t + t^2)e^{-5t}$;

(d) $x = 4\cos t + \sin t + e^{-t}$;

(e) $x = \frac{23}{18}\sin 3t - \frac{5}{18}\cos 3t + \frac{5}{18}e^{-3t}$;

(f) $x = \left(\frac{3}{4}\cos\sqrt{2}t - \frac{2}{2\sqrt{2}}\sin\sqrt{2}t\right)e^{-t} + \frac{1}{4}\cos t + \frac{1}{4}\sin t$.

3 (a) $x = Ae^{-3t} + Be^{-t} + \frac{c}{3}, x \to \frac{c}{3}$;

(b) $x = Ae^{-3t} + Be^{-t} + \frac{1}{8}e^{t}, x \to \infty$;

(c) $x = Ae^{-3t} + Be^{-t} + \frac{1}{2}te^{-t}, x \to 0$.

4 (a) $x = -\frac{1}{6}\sin 2t + a\cos 2t + \frac{1}{3}\sin t$;

(b) $x = \frac{1}{8}\sin 2t + a\cos 2t - \frac{1}{4}t\cos 2t$.

5 $x = \frac{a}{3}\cos nt - \frac{a}{3}\cos 2nt$.

6 $\frac{\mu g}{n^2}, x = ut - \frac{u}{n}\sin nt, 2u$.

7 $\ddot{x} + 4\omega\dot{x} + 5\omega^2 x = 0$.

8 $\ddot{x} + 4\omega\dot{x} + 5\omega^2 x = 0, C = 5a, \sec\phi = \frac{5}{3}$.

9 (a) (i) $x = A\sin\omega t + B\cos\omega t$,

(ii) $x = A\sin\omega t + B\cos\omega t - \frac{at}{2\omega}\cos\omega t$;

(b) (i) $x = \frac{a}{2\omega^2}\sin\omega t - \frac{at}{2\omega}\cos\omega t$.

10 $x = ae^{-3nt}(1 - \cos 3nt)$.

11 $\ddot{x} + 2\omega\dot{x} + 2\omega^2 x = 0, C = 2a, \alpha = -\frac{\pi}{3}, t = \frac{1}{\omega}\left(\frac{\pi}{12} + n\pi\right)$.

12 $x = -\frac{1}{75}(2\sin 10t - \sin 20t)$.

13 $a = 13, \omega = \frac{\pi}{8}, \phi = \tan^{-1}\left(\frac{12}{5}\right), \dot{x} = -\frac{3}{2}\pi, \ddot{x} = \frac{5\pi^2}{64} t = 8$.

14 $x = \sin\omega t + 2a\cos\omega t - \frac{1}{2}\sin 2\omega t$.

15 $x = \frac{1}{9}e^{-t}(3 + \sin 3t)$.

4 Impulsive motion

EXERCISE 4A

1 7.2 N.

2 (b) 19.92 N s^{-1}.

3 (a) $26\mathbf{i} + 8\mathbf{j} + 2\mathbf{k}$; **(b)** $0\mathbf{i} + 0\mathbf{j}$; **(c)** $(3\ln 3 - 2)\mathbf{i}$.

4 (b) $a = -\frac{9mu}{8T^3} - \frac{3mg}{2T^2}, b = \frac{9mu}{4T^3} - \frac{3mg}{T}, c = 0$;

(c) $F_{max} = \frac{3mg}{2} - \frac{9mu}{8T}$.

5 **(b)** $\frac{1}{3}$; **(c)** **(i)** 0.002 s.

6 **(a)** $\frac{5mu}{2}$; **(b)** $\frac{5mu}{2} + mg$; **(c)** $3.93mu + 1.57mg$.

7 **(a)** 5130 N s upwards; **(b)** 6894 N s;
(c) $F_{max} = 6122.25$ N.

8 **(a)** $1.32a$; **(b)** 0.245 N s; **(c)** 0.214.

9 **(a)** 80 kN; **(b)** 20kN.

EXERCISE 4B

1 $v_p = \frac{2}{3}u\sqrt{3}$, $v_q = u\sqrt{\frac{7}{3}}$.

2 u, $mu\sqrt{3}$.

3 $v_p = \frac{10}{7}$ ms^{-1}, $v_q = \frac{4}{7}\sqrt{43}$ ms^{-1}, $I = \frac{20}{7}$ N s.

4 **(b)** $\frac{4}{3}m\sqrt{gc}$; **(c)** $\frac{17c}{9}$; **(d)** $\frac{4}{3}mgc$.

5 **(a)** $\frac{g}{5}, \frac{12mg}{5}$; **(c)** $\frac{9mv}{8}$; **(d)** $\frac{15mv^2}{16}$ **(e)** $\frac{1}{\sqrt{3}}$.

6 $a = \frac{g}{7}$, $T = \frac{24mg}{7}$;

(a) $\frac{7v}{9}$; **(b)** $\frac{8mV}{9}$; **(c)** $\frac{49V^2}{18g}$.

7 **(a)** **(i)** $\frac{1}{2}u$, **(ii)** $\frac{1}{3}$, **(iii)** $\frac{5}{6}mu^2$;

(b) **(i)** $\frac{3}{8}v$, **(ii)** $\frac{15}{8}mv$, **(iii)** $\frac{15}{16}mv^2$.

8 $T = \frac{2Mmg}{(M+m)}, \frac{1}{\sqrt{2}}$.

9 $a = \frac{1}{5}g$, $T = 8mg$;

(a) $\frac{1}{3}d$; **(b)** $\frac{2}{3}\sqrt{\frac{10d}{g}}$; **(c)** $\sqrt{\frac{gd}{10}}$.

10 $\frac{J}{7m}, \frac{5J}{17m}, \frac{12J}{17}$.

5 Motion with variable mass

EXERCISE 5A

1 $V_0 + U\ln\frac{10}{9}$.

2 $v = U\ln\left(\frac{M_0}{M_0 - kt}\right) - gt$, $U\ln 2 - \frac{gM_0}{2k}$.

3 $v = \frac{g}{k}\ln\frac{10}{9} - \frac{g}{10k}$, $h = \frac{19g}{200k^2} - \frac{9g}{10k^2}\ln\frac{10}{9}$.

5 **(a)** $v = -gt - U\ln(1 - kt)$; **(b)** $v = -gt - U\ln\left[1 - \frac{\lambda}{kM_0}(1 - e^{-kt})\right]$;

(c) $v = (kU - g)t$; **(d)** $m = M_0e^{-\left(\frac{g+k}{U}\right)t}$.

6 (a) When mass of barrel has halved.

7 (b) (i) $7g$.

EXERCISE 5B

1 (a) $v = \frac{g}{2k}\left[1 + kt - \frac{1}{1+kt}\right]$;

(b) $v = \frac{g}{k}\left[1 - e^{-kt}\right]$;

(c) $v = \dfrac{gt(k-\lambda) + \frac{\lambda g}{k}\left(e^{kt} - 1\right)}{k + \lambda(e^{kt} - 1)}$;

(d) $v^2 = \frac{2g}{3k}\left[1 + kx - \frac{1}{(1+kx)^2}\right]$;

(e) $v^2 = \frac{g}{k}(1 - e^{-2kx})$.

2 $v = \frac{g}{3k}\left(1 - e^{-3kt}\right)$, $v_{\max} = \frac{g}{3k}$.

3 $v^2 = \frac{g}{2k}\left(1 - e^{-2kx}\right)$, $v = \sqrt{\frac{63g}{128k}}$, $x = \frac{1}{k}\ln 8$.

4 $2M_0$, $\frac{U^2}{g}(2 - \ln 2)$.

5 $\frac{3}{2}M_0$, $\frac{U^2}{g}(1 - \ln \frac{9}{4})$.

6 Circular motion with variable speed

EXERCISE 6A

1 $2.55\,\text{m}\,\text{s}^{-2}$.

2 (a) $2.46\,\text{m}\,\text{s}^{-2}$, **(b)** $1.86\,\text{m}\,\text{s}^{-2}$.

3 $2.27\,\text{m}\,\text{s}^{-2}$.

4 $19.0\,\text{m}\,\text{s}^{-1}$.

5 $110\,\text{m}$.

6 (a) $\frac{25a}{2}$; **(b)** $\frac{V^2\sqrt{126}}{a}$.

7 $x = \frac{a}{\Omega\mu}\ln(\Omega\mu t + 1)$.

8 $t = \frac{u}{\mu g}$.

9. $8.74\,\text{m}\,\text{s}^{-2}$.

EXERCISE 6B

1 (a) $3.97\,\text{m}\,\text{s}^{-1}$, $932\,\text{N}$; **(b)** $799\,\text{N}$.

2 (a) $4.65\,\text{m}\,\text{s}^{-1}$, $0.05\,\text{N}$; **(b)** $2.99\,\text{N}$.

3 (a) $556\,\text{N}$; **(b)** $48.0°$.

4 $2.56\,\text{m}\,\text{s}^{-1}$, $435\,\text{N}$.

5 $3234\,\text{N}$, $1666\,\text{N}$.

6 $2.21\,\text{m}\,\text{s}^{-1}$.

7 $4.58\,\text{rad}\,\text{s}^{-1}$.

8 $3mg\sin\theta$.

9 $\frac{a}{3}$.

11 (a) $\sqrt{\frac{4rg}{3}}$; **(b) (i)** $\frac{mg}{3}$, **(ii)** $\frac{29mg}{6}$.

12 (a) $\sqrt{5gl}$; **(b)** $\left(\sqrt{5} - 2\right)\sqrt{gl}$.

EXERCISE 6C

1 0.159 m.

2 Not valid; as period does not depend on mass.

3 0.777 s.

4 Reduced length by 1.4%.

5 Same periods, different amplitudes.

6 At rest $\theta = \frac{\pi}{36}\cos(7t)$, pushed $\theta = 0.113\cos(7t - 0.686)$.

7 **(a)** 99.3 cm; **(b)** Reduce by 0.14 cm.

8 75%.

9 **(a)** $\theta = \frac{\pi}{30}\cos\left(\sqrt{\frac{9.8}{3}}t\right)$; **(b)** 0.729 s.

10 **(a)** $\theta = \frac{\pi}{50}\cos(20t)$; **(b)** $v = -\frac{\pi g}{1000}\sin(20t)$.

11 **(c)** $2\pi\sqrt{\frac{2a}{g}}$; **(d)** $\frac{\pi}{2}\sqrt{\frac{a}{g}}\left(1+\sqrt{2}\right)$.

12 **(a)** 1.27 s; **(b)** $9.34\,\text{m s}^{-2}$;

(c) Increased as g is inversely proportional to the square of the distance from the centre of the Earth.

Exam style practice paper

1 79.0°.

2 $\mathbf{F} = 6\mathbf{i} + 2\mathbf{j} + 4\mathbf{k}$, $\mathbf{G} = -3\mathbf{i} + 16\mathbf{j} - 8\mathbf{k}$.

3 **(a)** 4.71 s; **(b)** 100 m; **(c)** $32.7\,\text{m s}^{-1}$.

4 **(a)** $\frac{32}{75}$; **(b)** 32.8 g.

5 **(b)** $v = \sqrt{\frac{2ag}{3}}$.

6 **(b)** Critically damped motion; **(c)** $x = \frac{l}{2}\left(\frac{ct}{2m} + 1\right)e^{-ct/2m}$.

7 **(b)** $U\ln(4) - 100g$.

Index